LOGICO-PHILOSOPHICAL STUDIES

LOGICO-
PHILOSOPHICAL
STUDIES

Edited by Albert Menne

D. REIDEL PUBLISHING COMPANY

DORDRECHT-HOLLAND

LOGISCH-PHILOSOPHISCHE STUDIEN

First published by Verlag Karl Alber

Freiburg | München

Partly translated by Horace S. Glover

1962

Printed in the Netherlands by D. Reidel, Dordrecht

CONTENTS

PREFACE OF THE EDITOR

This work will offer students and all those interested in contemporary philosophy an easily accessible collection of logico-philosophical studies, through whose use they can become acquainted with the logical calculus, no longer in its theoretical and abstract form but in its application to philosophical problems. We become vitally aware that such selected problems, which had already emerged in ancient or scholastic philosophy, belong to the existence of the *philosophia perennis*. The trail-blazing research in this direction was accomplished most of all by I. M. Bocheński and the essays included in the present work, besides being indeed distinguished through their thematic unity, are also distinguished in that they were either written by I. M. Bocheński or written in his spirit and are the continuation of problems raised by him.

Chapter I clarifies without formal means the relation between classical, traditional and symbolic logic. Chapter II contains the proof that Aristotelian logic is not only faultless but even comprises an especially beautiful part of formal logic. Chapter III shows how the representation of a simplicity, as is seldom reached in logic, is obtained through a suitable introduction of a new symbol and corresponding definitions. Chapter IV then shows how the system can be interpreted as a genuine constituent of the logical calculus and refers to several ontological consequences of further results of modern syllogistic research. Chapter V points out that there are methods for the solution of the antinomies, which, developed by the Scholastics, are susceptible to strict formalization and diverge sharply from the customary. In Chapter VI it is shown that in the area of symbolic logic there exist unlimited possibilities, especially with regard to the treatment of ethical questions, as opposed to the usual equating of symbolic logic and a philosophical system. Chapter VII examines the concept of existence and shows that it is not defined, in the neopositivistic way, *only* through the existence operator. Chapter VIII offers a new analysis of the Thomistic concept of analogy. In this the author has also succeeded in furnishing a proof that a syllogism containing a so-called analogical middle term is valid. Finally, Chapter IX presents a formalization of some aspects of the problem of universals in the area of logistic and with regard to contemporary problems; here also, it was possible to attain a far-reaching, precise formulation and at the same time to point out that a series of views on these questions is inadequate.

With that, a two-fold goal appears to have been attained: on the one hand, it has been shown that some classical problems and solutions of *philosophia perennis* not only are not meaningless, as has been asserted many times, but that, to the contrary, they can be treated by means which are *more penetrating* than those of many positivists. On the other hand, it has been demonstrated how fruitful the application of logical methods to these problems can be.

Repeatedly, one hears the theme that symbolic logic is a logic only for the mathematician, only a special logic applicable to mathematics or only a special branch of mathematics, unfruitful and uninteresting for the 'genuine' logician and philosopher. By common agreement, the prejudice has been given the unhappy designation 'mathematical logic', which name has in recent years unfortunately included more and more in it. I may therefore be permitted to propose the following terminology: the ancient and Scholastic form of logic be called *classical logic;* the prevailing spinning-out of this logic since the *Logique du Port Royal* and its mixture of psychological and epistemological trimmings, as it was generally taught around the turn of the century, be termed *traditional logic;* the modern logical calculus is dubbed in English *symbolic logic*, and may be called in German *logistic;* by *modern logic* we shall understand, then, the whole of the symbolic logic, the still familiar classical logic and the formal ingredient of traditional logic. For between these three forms of logic there exists no real antithesis: the fundamental problems and results are to a great extent common to them although they are differentiated through their direction of interests and manner of representation. Because of this, the formalized language of symbolic logic as a means of representation certainly exceeds both other forms. Therefore, classical and traditional theory can be made more precise logistically and its consequences more easily examined, as some chapters of this book so well demonstrate.

But principally, this book has been published to point out that classical logic through logistic treatment has very interesting results and problems to offer the philosopher and to show that a series of philosophical problems can be greatly clarified through the methodological means offered by modern logic. Hence, it is unfortunate in many ways that a lively interest in modern logic on the part of the philosopher has not been awakened. The indifference of many philosophers appears to be conditioned, namely, not only because of faintheartedness engendered by the laborious work in the calculus – of which this book presents some harmless examples – but much more because of ignorance of the methodological possibilities offered by the logical calculus in its application to philosophical problems.

I wish to thank Messrs. I. M. Bocheński, I. Thomas and P. Banks for kindly making available to me their already partially published works. I have left them essentially unaltered although, however, further progress has been made in various areas; in only a few places are there slight modifications, especially in associated footnotes where I allude to recent literature. It appears to me that the substance of these studies is rarely surpassed; it is concerned with, so to speak, the point of departure which must be assimilated by the student if he would go further. All that is necessary for such a further study he will find in the excellent, running bibliography of the *Journal of Symbolic Logic*.

A. MENNE

Hamburg, May 1962

P. BANKS

ON THE PHILOSOPHICAL INTERPRETATION OF LOGIC: AN ARISTOTELIAN DIALOGUE*

Dramatis Personae: Mr Paleo, Mr Neo and The Aristotelian

Mr Paleo: I am fed up with all this logistic – a mechanical game with symbols, and a corruption of all logic. The rise of logistic is to me one of the symptoms of the decay of our culture. People do not want to think any more, they just calculate.

Mr Neo: My dear Mr Paleo, I am afraid you have never tried to work out any proofs in logistic, for if you had you could not possibly say such things. Not less, but rather more thought is required in our domain, and if we use formalism it is in order to render the tremendous task of thought less arduous, indeed possible.

The Aristotelian: I must say that I agree with our friend Mr Neo. And I would like to add the following remark. One who reads Aristotle – and not only the *Logique du Port Royal* as I fear is the case with most of you fellows of the Paleo group – is always struck by the very Aristotelian spirit which pervades recent mathematical logic. I shall say more. I find nothing in recent philosophy which is more genuinely Aristotelian than the speculations of Mr Neo and his friends, both in logic proper and in its applications.

Mr Paleo: Well I never! How is it possible that you who claim to be an Aristotelian can approve of a school which destroys the very foundations of Aristotelian logic?

Mr Neo: I am much obliged to you, Mr Aristotelian, for your intended compliment to us logisticians; but I must say that I agree with Mr Paleo to the extent that I cannot see how an Aristotelian can possibly support recent logic, which has overthrown nearly every detail of your master's work.

The Aristotelian: How interesting! And may I know at least some of those details which the logisticians have so successfully overthrown? I must

* First published in *Dominican Studies III* (1950) 139–153.

confess that I am rather fond of logistic myself, but I never noticed anything of that kind in it.

Mr Paleo: Come, Mr Aristotelian! You are exaggerating. Do you really deny that logistic is completely and radically anti-Aristotelian?

The Aristotelian: Most emphatically I do.

Mr Neo: Now look here: Aristotle teaches an absurd substantialist theory, our logic is based on a theory of events. Aristotle is a realist, we are thorough-going nominalists. Aristotle would reduce all sentences to the unique attributive form '*S* is *P*', we know that this is wrong. Aristotle claims that all logical laws can be reduced to the syllogism, we have discovered that this is a completely mistaken view. Aristotle believes in evident axioms, we have got rid of them. Is all that not enough to prove that our logic has nothing to do with Aristotelianism?

Mr Paleo: Yes. I seldom agree with Mr Neo, but I must say I am completely on his side here.

The Aristotelian: Your set of arguments looks very impressive indeed, and I have certainly read all that in some books. However I have got – perhaps out of the study of the *Prior Analytics* – perhaps from my prolonged speculations about mathematical logic – that bad habit of not taking the words at their face-value, but of investigating how they can be justified. And I am afraid I never could find any justification at all for what you say, Mr Neo.

Mr Paleo: That is the most astounding thing I ever heard about logic. Would you be so kind as to make yourself a little more explicit? Perhaps we could take the contradictions mentioned by Mr Neo and discuss them one by one.

The Aristotelian: Very well. Let us start with what Mr Neo calls that absurd substantialistic view of the world. Do you really believe that recent logic supports an opposite view?

Mr Neo: Most certainly it does. Do we not base our logical systems on a theory of unanalysed sentences which represent facts, events, and not substances?

The Aristotelian: Well, I am not so sure that you are right. For what you mean by an unanalysed sentence is not so much a sentence as a variable, i.e. a frame for a sentence. And what such a sentence may be is by no means decided by any theory of deduction. If you would have a look at the *Principia* you will find that Whitehead and Russell suppose as a

2

normal form of sentence for which their '*p*', '*q*', '*r*' etc. stand, precisely '$\phi \ ! \ a$', i.e. a sentence in which a property is attributed to an individual. Now individual is what Aristotle calls 'substance', first substance of course.

Mr Paleo: Nevertheless the very idea of basing logic on such relations as implication between sentences is completely un-Aristotelian.

The Aristotelian: Is it? I am not so sure of it. But first of all it seems to me that logistic is by no means based on the so-called theory of deduction.

Mr Neo: Then on what is it based?

The Aristotelian: On metalogical rules. And if you consider those metalogical rules, you will find that they are different formulations either of the *dictum de omni* or of the principle of identity. Some of your friends, Mr Neo, are accustomed to talk about 'tautologies'; I dislike the expression very much for it is misleading, but it covers the correct intuition that some kind of identity lies at the bottom of recent logic.

Mr Neo: But, Mr Aristotelian, you should not forget that logistic is operationalist.

Mr Aristotelian: What do you mean by that?

Mr Neo: I mean that by '$\phi \ a$' we do not understand the attribution of a property ϕ to a thing a, but of an operation ϕ on the symbol 'a'.

The Aristotelian: Well, Mr Neo, I have a great esteem for your properly logical studies, but it seems to me that you have not yet got into the depths of what we nowadays call 'semiotics', otherwise you could not possibly – excuse the word – talk such nonsense.

Mr Neo: What nonsense did I talk?

The Aristotelian: You were confusing language with metalanguage. We can say in metalanguage that we apply some operation to a symbol, but then we are talking about symbols; we cannot make such a statement in the language proper, when symbols are *used* and not mentioned. In logistic, which is a language, '$\phi \ a$' means only this: 'the object a has the property ϕ'. That property may be an operation, but it will be an operation of the object, not of the logician. When we say '$\phi \ a$' we say that a property belongs to an object.

Mr Paleo: I fear you are giving an Aristotelian twist to logistic. The logisticians themselves do not think as you do.

The Aristotelian: May I ask you for names?

Mr Paleo: I thought they were all of the operationalist opinion.

3

The Aristotelian: You are completely wrong here. As far as I know, not a single great logician ever thought in that way, at least when he was doing logic; for you will be aware that some logicians also philosophize. No, operationalism is a philosophical theory imposed upon recent logic by some philosophers. It has nothing to do with logic itself, and is even opposed to its spirit.

Mr Neo: Well, perhaps you are right on that point. Nevertheless I shall remind you that our modern mind is profoundly opposed to the substantialistic view. I may quote Whitehead as an instance.

The Aristotelian: But we are not discussing the modern mind; we are talking about logic. And while no one ever went farther than Whitehead in dissolving substance, yet his logic presupposes at every step individuals with properties, i.e. substances.

Mr Paleo: You are always mentioning individuals; but the Aristotelian teaching admits also universals. Now logistic is, as Mr Neo rightly said, thoroughly nominalistic.

The Aristotelian: Really, Mr Paleo! Where did you find that?

Mr Paleo: It seems to be a quite trivial truth.

Mr Neo: I must say I am in complete agreement with Mr Paleo; I am a nominalist myself and so are practically all of us.

The Aristotelian: You will excuse me. Are you excluding me from the respectable family of modern logicians?

Mr Neo: By no means. I only thought you were a nominalist too.

Mr Paleo: That is also what is generally thought in my group.

The Aristotelian: And why, please?

Mr Paleo: Because you are a logistician.

The Aristotelian: I really like you, Mr Paleo. It is capital. All logisticians are nominalists. Why? Because every one of them is a nominalist; and why is every logistician a nominalist? Because he is a logistician. Aristotle, Mr Paleo, would not be very pleased with the rigour of your argument.

Mr Paleo: Joking apart, Mr Aristotelian, there are many proofs to support my assertion. For one, most eminent logisticians profess nominalism.

The Aristotelian: That is true of a certain number; and some of them, in saying they are nominalists, really mean it.

Mr Neo: What do you mean?

4

The Aristotelian: I mean that many of them are not nominalists at all. Professors Quine and Goodman, for instance, claim to be nominalists while simply fighting Platonism. Now you will know, Mr Paleo, that one who is not a Platonist does not have to be a nominalist. I dare say that you are yourself a case in point.

Mr Paleo: Most certainly.

Mr Neo: But you will not deny that the Vienna school, at least, was nominalistic; so is Professor Tarski; so is Mr Ayer.

The Aristotelian: I object to putting Mr Ayer in the same class as Professor Tarski in this regard. He has not distinguished himself by logical work as Tarski has. But I agree that *some* important logicians are nominalist now, as some have always been. *Nil novi sub sole.*

Mr Paleo: All logisticians, Mr Aristotelian, not some.

The Aristotelian: I am sorry to have to contradict you. Most of the leading logisticians are most certainly *not* nominalists. They even seem to be Platonists.

Mr Neo: Who for instance?

The Aristotelian: Most of the founders; Lord Russell in his first period, Whitehead (most radically,) Lukasiewicz, Fraenkel, Scholz, Frege and so on.

Mr Paleo: I can hardly believe you. I thought everyone knew that all logisticians are nominalists.

The Aristotelian: Everyone who has never read recent logic, yet feels entitled to write and talk about it. If you do not believe me, take Professor Beth's useful collection of the *effata platonica* of leading logicians.

Mr Neo: I dislike arguments from authority. Let us go into the matter itself. You mentioned the papers of Professors Quine and Goodman; do you not think they have shown the nominalism not of logisticians but of logistics itself?

The Aristotelian: Just the opposite, Mr Neo. What those brilliant logicians have shown is that the logic of the *Principia* is thoroughly Platonic. They have put up a decent fight in order to get rid of this Platonism, and I am sorry to say that they have not been completely successful. I hope that in working in their line we shall be able to get rid of Platonism, which is a nuisance.

Mr Paleo: Yet I am not convinced. Aristotelian logic deals with universal concepts; logistic substitutes classes for them. Where an Aristotelian says

5

'man' and means the universal concept, logisticians say 'all men'. Now this is nominalism.

The Aristotelian: I do not think so. I believe that one of the most fundamental principles of Aristotelian philosophy is that all ultimate real subjects are individual. An Aristotelian cannot stop at such universal concepts as your Man. He is bound to analyse it into many individual men all having some common attribute.

Mr Paleo: But logistic denies the existence of common properties.

The Aristotelian: By no means. How could it? If it deals with classes, it must define them by properties. Mr Neo can testify that a class is defined in logistic as the set of objects possessing in common a given property. In other words, the universal has not been eliminated from logic.

Mr Paleo: But what about the method? I understand it is purely verbal; you are interested in words only. This is a nominalism of a very radical type.

Mr Neo: Well, Mr Paleo, I thought I was a nominalist, but I would not go as far as that. Symbols that we use always have some meaning. It is true that we abstract from the meaning while operating with symbols, but *abstrahentium non est mendacium,* as you say.

Mr Paleo: You may be right. But what about the corruption of the Aristotelian scheme of the judgment, by the introduction of the so-called 'relative sentences'?

Mr Neo: Yes. I do not call it a corruption, but such an amplification that practically nothing is left of Aristotelianism in our recent logic.

The Aristotelian: So you believe. It is once again not my opinion. I think that the whole fabric of recent logic is perfectly Aristotelian, if not Platonic.

Mr Paleo: This looks like one more of your paradoxes.

The Aristotelian: It looks so only to people who neither read Aristotle nor take the trouble to think over logistic. To me who has done both it is not a paradox but a rather evident truth.

Mr Neo: Please explain. Your assertion may not be paradoxical, but you will agree it is opposed to what logisticians generally hold.

The Aristotelian: I am afraid it is; yet it seems easy to show it to be correct. What I am asserting is that every single law of logistic is constructed according to the Aristotelian scheme of subject and attribute.

Mr Neo: How? It seems to me quite evident that such sentences as 'John loves Mary' have nothing to do with this scheme.

6

The Aristotelian: Really, Mr Neo? Let us see. What are you saying when you assert that John loves Mary? That the relation of love holds, as we say, between those two persons; in other words, that the relation *is* in them; it is their attribute, it is asserted of them – just as Aristotle teaches.

Mr Neo: Not at all, Mr Aristotelian. Love is not an attribute of John, as his colour or his weight is. It is a relation. For the copula quite a different thing has been substituted. John is linked to Mary not as an attribute to a subject, but as one relative term to another.

Mr Paleo: Well, but it is easy to transform your sentence into 'John is loving Mary'.

Mr Neo: Yes, you can do it. But I do not see why we should torture the quite natural sentence 'John loves Mary' into so artificial a scheme.

The Aristotelian: I do not think there is a fundamental difference between your views. Of course Mr Neo is right when he says that in practice we do not need to transform his sentence; but why should you forbid Mr Paleo this transformation if it is needed to show his interpretation?

Mr Neo: Because this would be an illegitimate introduction of metaphysical considerations into logic.

The Aristotelian: No, Mr Neo, I do not ask you to effect the transformation at each step in your logical deductions; but you cannot deny that both formulae are equivalent. You know that the *Principia* supplies sufficient means to effect the transformation.

Mr Neo: Of course it does.

The Aristotelian: Well, if so, why quarrel? Mr Paleo and myself see the ontological structure of the world as one of individuals with properties. If we can show that each sentence can be brought to exhibit this structure, we show that our view cannot be challenged by logic.

Mr Neo: But you are not going to deny that there *is* a difference between such sentences as 'John loves Mary' and 'John is good'?

Mr Paleo: I do. It is exactly the same structure, if well understood.

The Aristotelian: Your are wrong, Mr Paleo. It is not the same structure. There you miss an important teaching of Aristotle himself.

Mr Paleo: What teaching?

The Aristotelian: The teaching according to which each category is predicated in a different way. Do you not see that if this is true of different absolute accidents, it must be the more true of the predication of a relation as contrasted with that of, say, a quality?

Mr Paleo: It certainly is a different predication, but nevertheless a predication.

The Aristotelian: There I agree with you. We assert the relation of the terms, we predicate its name. But it is not the same kind of predication as in other cases. The relation contains an *esse ad* as Scholastics say: logistic only explicitates this teaching on the logical level.

Mr Neo: Mr Aristotelian, I fear you are going to reduce the whole of our ogic to the meagre *Barbara-Celarant*.

The Aristotelian: Have no fear, Mr Neo. I have no such aims. If you had read the *Organon*, you would know that there is more in Aristotle than modern logicians, especially Mr Paleo's friends, ever dreamed of. There are, for instance, some very interesting theses of the logic of relations; there are some laws of the logic of propositions, one even with variables; there is an analysis of the sentence as a formal implication, and so on. But who reads Aristotle to-day? You, Mr Neo, think that it is enough to know logistics; Mr Paleo is of the opinion that the *Logique du Port Royal* suffices.

Mr Neo: I am glad that you agree with me at least to the extent of thinking that the *Barbara, Celarant*, etc., make up only a very small part of logic. (Though, in fact, the system is false.)

Mr Paleo: It is not false at all; only you deal with it mechanically, and thus, not understanding the rules of supposition, you think you have proved that *Darapti* and similar moods are wrong.

The Aristotelian: For once, Mr Paleo, I am of your opinion; only I disagree with your way of supporting it.

Mr Paleo: And how are you going to establish the validity of the disputed moods without the theory of supposition?

The Aristotelian: I am not going to establish it, because the proof has already been given, by a purely axiomatic method. Mr Neo will surely have read papers on the subject, in *Dominican Studies,* or Dr Popper's treatment.

Mr Neo: I am sorry, I have not; for I do not see the importance of the topic.

The Aristotelian: The importance of syllogistic theory is far greater than people generally believe. Have you ever tried to analyse such reasonings as are to be found, say, in newspapers, or in geological works? I have, and I found that different moods of syllogism are in frequent use.

Mr Neo: Anyway, syllogistic is not the whole of logic, and so the Aristotelian teaching that the *dictum de omni* is a fundamental principle is certainly false.

The Aristotelian: No, Mr Neo, I do not think so. I am firmly persuaded that it plays a very important, even quite fundamental role in logistic.

Mr Neo: How is that?

The Aristotelian: Because the rule of substitution, without which you can hardly do anything in logistic, is nothing else than a metalogical transposition of the *dictum*.

Mr Neo: True, but that is metalogic. In logic itself the *dictum* is not needed.

The Aristotelian: You touch there on an important point. Recent logic is certainly far more differentiated than the older one was. We know now that it contains different levels and far more parts than was thought before. I am not one of those who deny every progress in logic.

Mr Paleo: But there has never been any such progress since Aristotle.

The Aristotelian: That is what Kant said, and it is amusing to find you, a defender of strict tradition, swearing by the words of such a master. But Kant was wrong here, as so often. We know to-day that there was considerable progress in logic at the time of the Stoics and again among the Scholastics; now we are again in the middle of a new period of rapid development. Really, Mr Paleo, only one who does not know anything about the contemporary state of logic can deny the enormous development of that science.

Mr Neo: You object to Mr Paleo, that he holds a Kantian thesis. But with your permission I shall say that an Aristotelian believing in scientific progress is a not less amusing person.

The Aristotelian: Why? Did not Aristotle create the history of ideas? Does not his theory of matter postulate a development? And can an Aristotelian proceed in any other way than by consulting experience? Really, Mr Neo, I fear you have a very inadequate idea of what Aristotelianism is.

Mr Neo: I am not interested in history; but as to our point, it seems that you are switching the discussion to metalogic.

The Aristotelian: Yes, and I have reasons for doing so. I believe in fact that genuine logic is what we call to-day the metalogical rules of a system.

Mr Neo: Why so?

9

The Aristotelian: Because logic is necessarily, though perhaps not primarily, a set of rules according to which a real reasoning is accomplished. Now a formalized system contains such rules only in its metalogical part.

Mr Neo: Do you mean to say that logic proper is of no use?

The Aristotelian: By no means! I only believe that much of it can be compared to an abacus of a very refined sort, I mean to a mechanical tool giving some useful results which may be interpreted in meaningful sentences. I think, indeed, that the status of many mathematical and even microphysical theories is just the same.

Mr Neo: And what do you deduce from it?

The Aristotelian: A refutation of what you said about the non-evidence of logical principles. If we agree that logic as understood by Aristotle, is our metalogic, you will see that most of your arguments against the evidence of logical principles become inefficient.

Mr Paleo: I can hardly believe that. Logisticians have many systems of logic which are opposed one to another – classical, intuitionistic, polyvalent, and yet others. They care nothing for evidence; they choose their axioms at random and each of them makes his own logic, or what he calls 'logic'. All this may be very amusing, but to me it looks like complete logical scepticism.

The Aristotelian: I do not think you are right. Look at the metalogical rules; one has never seen any intuitionistic or polyvalent sets of metalogical rules.

Mr Neo: Astounding though it be, Mr Paleo gave us a very exact description of what happens in contemporary logistic.

The Aristotelian: It is not astounding at all; he simply read one or two of Professor Carnap's propaganda-pamphlets. That is what Mr Paleo always does. But you, Mr Neo, should be better informed.

Mr Neo: I dare say I am, and still I believe Mr Paleo is right on this point.

The Aristotelian: There is of course something to be said for what he asserts. For one thing, it is certain that axiomatic connection is more important for a modern logician than it was for Aristotle; he will even abandon the evidence of his axioms when he can obtain something more beautifully coherent without it.

Mr Neo: Well, that does not seem very Aristotelian. And what about polyvalent logics? What about the principle of excluded middle?

The Aristotelian: That principle is perhaps the most difficult point in the philosophy of logic. Before starting any discussion I would say that people who have doubts about its validity are very Aristotelian indeed.

Mr Paleo: But, my dear sir, this is most certainly quite a new kind of Aristotelianism.

The Aristotelian: I said 'Aristotelian', not 'Port-Royalist' or 'John-of-St-Thomist'. Aristotelian it is. There is, Mr Paleo, a rather interesting booklet called '*Peri Hermeneias*'; I would advise you to read it; it is better than the *Logique du Port Royal;* much better in fact.

Mr Paleo: Well, I know Aristotle wrote such a book.

The Aristotelian: Yes, he did. And there in the ninth chapter, he questions the validity of the principle of excluded middle. I can say more. Professor Łukasiewicz, who does not claim to be a traditionalist as you do, read this chapter; and it was there he found the inspiration for his trivalent logic.

Mr Neo: You may be right, but still you know enough logic not to overlook the fact that the negation of the principle of excluded middle is not possible in the framework of a classical bivalent logic. So as we have some systems without this principle, there are several radically different logics to-day. And that is why I refuse to agree that we are still Aristotelian.

The Aristotelian: Don't be rash, Mr Neo. Do you really believe that Professor Łukasiewicz denies the validity of the principle of excluded middle?

Mr Neo: Of course he does, as far as his system is concerned.

The Aristotelian: Be careful, Mr Neo, be careful. That is the logician's highest virtue. Professor Łukasiewicz says that a sentence may have either the value *1,* or the value *1/2,* or the value *0,* does he not?

Mr Neo: It is so.

The Aristotelian: Does he admit that there is a third possibility besides these two: that a sentence in his system should or should not have the value *1*?

Mr Neo: No, if it is a real sentence.

The Aristotelian: Well, that means that he admits the principle of excluded middle.

Mr Neo: Mr Aristotelian! You were but now accusing operationalists of confusing language with metalanguage; now you are doing the same.

The Aristotelian: By no means, Mr Neo. I am very conscious of the

11

difference. What I say here is only this: for no system is there a set of metalogical rules which are themselves trivalent or intuitionistic, or, generally speaking, un-Aristotelian.

Mr Neo: Why not? We can formalize our metalanguage, and give it e.g. an intuitionistic form.

The Aristotelian: Most certainly we can; but once we do it, we must use some meta-metalinguistic rules. In any case the whole fabric will ultimately be built on some non-formalized rules, and of those I affirm that they are always bivalent.

Mr Neo: Why should they be?

The Aristotelian: I did not say they *should,* but only that they *are.* Can you show me a single system with non-evident, non-Aristotelian rules of deduction? A system whose rules violate, say, the principle of contradiction?

Mr Neo: You seem to be more empiricist than I am myself. For I believe that brute facts cannot decide in such matters.

The Aristotelian: Of course they cannot. But they show one thing, that the burden of proof is yours, Mr Neo, not ours. The situation is that *nobody ever* used any new kind of logic other than the Aristotelian.

Mr Neo: Not so quickly, Mr Aristotelian. Metalogical rules, not logic. It is not the same.

The Aristotelian: Now perhaps you understand why I said that logic, genuine logic, which is the set of laws in accordance with which we must reason if we wish to reason correctly, is not identical with the language of logistics. Logic, genuine logic, is only the set of metalogical rules.

Mr Paleo: I do not understand what you mean by all your meta-things, and doubt very much if they have any use. And if you deny that contemporary logistic is logic, then perhaps you agree with me.

The Aristotelian: No, Mr Paleo, I don't. I think that logistic, as far as its language is concerned, is just an abacus. But some such might be very interesting and useful. Moreover a good part of logistic can be translated into real logic, for instance the whole of *Principia Mathematica.*

Mr Paleo: And so what? Are you not back at the old Aristotelian starting-point? Why this enormous waste of time and energy on the calculus?

The Aristotelian: No, Mr Paleo, you are wrong. Contemporary logistic contains more, far more, than all older logic. I mean even in laws which are translatable into real rules of reasoning.

12

Mr Paleo: What is more than the old logic, is wrong.

The Aristotelian: No, it is often very good. Once more I must tell you: *tolle, lege.* None who has read them can deny the importance of recent studies, the enormous extension and refinement of formal logic accomplished by this work. And yet it remains fundamentally Aristotelian.

Mr Paleo: You seem to be a satisfied philosopher; I would call you a satisfied Aristotelian.

The Aristotelian: In one way I am satisfied. I find that the human mind, every time it engages in a serious speculative task, finds again and again the same eternal principles the most fundamental of which were discovered by 'the Master of those who know' as Dante called him. Logistic is surely a domain where this is most evident.

Mr Neo: And how are you dissatisfied?

The Aristotelian: I am dissatisfied with the situation in philosophy. People who should develop their Aristotelian heritage are amusing themselves with existentialisms and other -isms instead of working. While those who work in logic – I mean Mr Neo and his friends – have got under the influence of philosophers most unworthy of the science of logic, partisans of other -isms in fact.

Mr Neo: But are you not yourself a partisan of Aristotelianism?

The Aristotelian: That is just an unfortunate name. There is nothing in Aristotelianism to be compared with other -isms. Aristotelianism is just commonsense and scientific spirit. It is faith in reason and experience, and acknowledgement of the possibility of unlimited progress on traditional foundations. In the philosophy of logic as elsewhere, Aristotelianism stands above the struggling factions.

Mr Paleo: Do you hope to convert our philosophers to that view?

The Aristotelian: Unfortunately not. Aristotelianism, precisely because it is as I describe it, because it is a balanced view of reality, will always be the creed of a small minority only. Others will run after Plato or Hume.

Mr Paleo: I am not running after Plato or Hume.

The Aristotelian: No. Mr Paleo, you are not. You are an Aristotelian, though I dare say one of a poor sort; one who keeps the letter, ignoring the spirit, and even the letter you do not know. Read the *Organon*, Mr Paleo, and do not forget the words of St Paul: 'Littera occidit, spiritus vivificat'.

POSTSCRIPT. This conversation having become known in authoritative circles, the Aristotelian has been excluded from two Academies of which he was formerly a member, that of Tradition and that of Science. It was stated in the first that a man who dares to read *Principia Mathematica* instead of the *Logique du Port Royal* is evidently a madman; while the board of the other declared that an Aristotelian could no longer be tolerated in the company of scholars who have proved once for all that all truth is relative, that of their own opinion included.

I. M. BOCHENSKI

ON THE CATEGORICAL SYLLOGISM *

The scope of the present paper is to develop a formal system of assertoric categorical syllogism (abridged as 'CS') and to discuss some problems connected with it. By this an improvement in the Thomistic statement of the theory is aimed at. Such an improvement seems to be needed for two reasons: (1) considerable progress has been achieved in formal logic in recent times; but many leading logicians being only slightly interested in CS and most Thomists having no knowledge at all of recent formal logic, these achievements are seldom applied to the traditional doctrine and, if they are, the applications are not known; (2) some objections have been raised against the traditional theory of CS which need to be examined on a more rigorous basis.

The opinion of the author is that recent mathematical logic [1] has not weakened but has considerably strengthened the traditional position of Thomists.[2] These methods will be applied here.

There will be two parts: (1) The Formal System, (2) Discussion of Some Philosophical Problems.

I. THE FORMAL SYSTEM

The symbolism used here is that of Professor Łukasiewicz.[3] Also the

---

* First published in *Dominican Studies I* (1948) 35–57.

[1] Among the best introductions to mathematical logic are: Bocheński-Menne, *Grundriss der Logistik*, 2nd ed. Paderborn 1962; A. Tarski, *Introduction to Logic*, New York 1941; W. V. O. Quine, *Mathematical Logic*, 3rd ed., New York 1951 (more technical); R. Feys, *Logistiek*, I, Antwerpen 1944 (perhaps the best, unfortunately in Dutch). Among older short books the following may be used: R. Carnap, *Abriß der Logistik*, Wien 1929; D. Hilbert u. W. Ackermann, *Grundzüge der theoretischen Logik*, 4th ed. Berlin 1959. – The classical treatise is: A. N. Whitehead and B. Russell, *Principia Mathematica*, 3 vols., 3rd ed. Cambridge 1950. A complete bibliography is to be found (for 1666–1935) in A. Church, *A Bibliography of Symbolic Logic*, The Journal of Symb. Logic, 1, 1936, 121–218; this is continued in the same journal.

[2] Cf. *La pensée catholique et la logique moderne*, Cracovie 1937; I. M. Bocheński, *Nove Lezioni di Logica simbolica*, Roma 1938; Th. Greenwood, *Les fondements de la logique symbolique*, Paris 1939.

[3] J. Łukasiewicz, *Elementy logiki matematycznej* (Polish = Elements of mathematical

method of deduction and the main ideas of the system of CS are his, among others the discovery that our axioms *15* and *16* can be used as the only axioms alongside with *Barbara* and one other mode.[1] But the metalogical introduction is the work of the author of this paper and so is the form in which the ideas of Professor Łukasiewicz are restated, the present system being formally different (in the choice of axioms) from his system. The whole discussion of the system is also new.

The choice of Łukasiewicz's symbolism and method is due to the fact that this is the most rigorous symbolism and method we know, indeed the only one which allows a complete formalization of a deduction.[2] The main ideas of the same logician on the theory of CS have been preferred to others because they supply an excellent basis for further discussion and are, at the same time, the most satisfactory from the point of view of simplicity and beauty.[3]

There will be six chapters in this part: (1) Metalogical introduction, (2) Rules and method of deduction, (3) Definitions and axioms, (4) Deduction, (5) Partial and alternative systems, (6) Unsolved problems.

logic), lithographed, Warsaw 1929. This is the fundamental work, but unfortunately it is no more to be found. The author of the present article, having lost his copy during the war, was obliged to reconstruct some of its contents by memory. German accounts of the main ideas of Prof. Łukasiewicz are given in the following papers: *Philosophische Bemerkungen zu mehrwertigen Systemen des Aussagenkalküls*, C. r. Soc. Sc. et Lettres de Varsovie, Cl. III, 23, 1930, 51–77; *Ein Vollständigkeitsbeweis des zweiwertigen Aussagenkalküls*, ibid. 24, 1932, 153–183; *Zur Geschichte der Aussagenlogik*, Erkenntnis 5, 1935/6 111–131; *Die Logik und das Grundlagenproblem*, ex.: F. Gonseth, *Entretiens de Zurich*, Zürich 1941, 82–108. See also the Italian book of the author quoted above.

[1] The idea of using our axioms 15 and 16 is Leibniz's, cf. L. Couturat, *La Logique de Leibniz*, Paris 1901, pp. 9f.

[2] This is due to the fact that the system is bracketless and pointless. We know of no quite rigorous rule for the transformation of brackets and groups of points needed in other systems.

[3] Among other systems of CS developed by means of mathematical logic we may quote K. Ajdukiewicz, *Zalozenia logiki tradcyjnej* (Polish – Presuppositions of traditional logic), Przegląd Filozoficzny 29. 1926/7, 200–229, and R. Feys, *Logistiek*, I, Antwerpen 1944, pp. 208f. Professor Ajdukiewicz's treatment is similar to the method of Professor Łukasiewicz, applied here, while that of Professor Feys is quite different. The former uses a special axiom (in our system: 16) while the latter has only a special definition of the 'existential' implication (17.511, p. 296). In that case, however, no complete system of traditional CS can be deduced with propositions containing non-existential or existential implication alone. Thus, in order to state the full traditional doctrine in Professor Feys' system it is necessary to use both, i.e. to admit, against the intuition, that there are two different meanings of the formula 'all *b*'s are *a*'s'. The method used here allows us to avoid this.

ON THE CATEGORICAL SYLLOGISM

1. Metalogical introduction

We are going to enumerate first the symbols which will be used in the system, with their names and an interpretation. Later on a set of metalogical definitions, useful for further discussion, will be stated.

Symbols	Names	Interpretation
D 1. 'p', 'q', 'r', 's'	propositional variables	letters indicating a void place where a proposition may be written.
D 2. 'N' followed by a proposition	negation	negation of the proposition which follows 'N'.
D 3. 'C' followed by two propositions	implication	conditional proposition.
D 4. 'K' followed by two propositions	conjunction	copulative proposition.
D 5. 'a', 'b', 'm'	nominal variables	letters indicating a void place where a name may be written.
D 6. 'A', 'I', 'E', 'O'	syllogistic operators	(as in traditional logic).
D 7. Syllogistic operator followed by two nominal variables	syllogistic proposition [1]	(as in traditional logic).
D 8. Symbols as under 1, 2, 3, 4 and 7	proposition	

Syllogistic proposition beginning with:

D 9. 'A'	A proposition	universal affirmative proposition.
D 10. 'I'	I proposition	particular affirmative proposition.

---

[1] This is not a quite correct name. We should have distinguished a proposition from a frame for a proposition; our syllogistic proposition is evidently a frame. But as full propositions never occur in formal logic (except with bound variables), there is no fear of confusion.

Symbols	Names	Interpretation
D 11. '*E*'	*E* proposition	universal negative proposition.
D 12. '*O*'	*O* proposition	particular negative proposition.

These are the only artificial symbols to be used. Out of them '*E*' and '*O*' will be defined, the others being primitive terms of our system; but again D 1.–4. belong to the logic of propositions. Thus there will be only five special primitive terms: '*a*', '*b*', '*m*', '*A*' and '*I*', the last two being the only constants among them.

Most of the following names, as also the above D 9.–12., will be used in the commentaries and in the discussion of the formal system, not in the system itself:

D 13. '*X* is the antecedent of *Y*' for: '*Y* is an implication and *X* is the first [1] proposition in *Y*'.

D 14. '*X* is the consequent of *Y*' for: '*Y* is an implication and *X* is the second proposition in *Y*'.

D 15. '*X* is a CS' for: '*X* is an implication whose antecedent is a product of two syllogistic propositions and the consequent another syllogistic proposition'.

D 16. '*X* is a mode' for: '*X* is a CS'[2].

D 17. '*X* is a premiss of *Y*' for: '*Y* is a CS and *X* is a syllogistic proposition contained in the antecedent of *Y*'.

D 18. '*X* is the conclusion of *Y*' for: '*Y* is a CS and *X* is the consequent of *Y*'.

D 19. '*X* is a term of *Y*' for: '*Y* is a syllogistic proposition and *X* is a nominal variable in *Y*'.

D 20. '*X* is the subject of *Y*' for: '*X* is the first term of *Y*'.

D 21. '*X* is the predicate of *Y*' for: '*X* is the second term of *Y*'.

D 22. '*X* is a major term of *Y*' for: '(1) *X* is the predicate of the conclusion of *Y* and in one of the premisses of *Y* there is a term of the same

---

[1] By 'first' we mean the proposition which immediately follows (without any intermediate symbol) the operator '*C*'.

[2] Same remark as p. 17, footnote 1. We should have distinguished a frame for a syllogism (a syllogistic mode) from a full syllogism. But as full syllogisms never occur in formal logic, we are going to use both names as meaning the same, for the sake of stylistic convenience.

form as X, or (2) X is a term of one of the premisses of Y and X has the same form as the predicate of the conclusion of Y'.[1]

D 23. 'X is a minor term of Y' for: '(1) X is the subject of the conclusion of Y and in one of the premisses of Y there is a term of the same form as X, or (2) X is a term of one of the premisses of Y and X has the same form as the subject of the conclusion of Y'.

D 24. 'X is a middle term of Y' for: 'X is a term of one of the premisses of Y and in the other premiss of Y there is a term of the same form as X'.

D 25. 'X is the major premiss of Y' for: 'X is a premiss of Y and a term of X is a major term of Y'.

D 26. 'X is the minor premiss of Y' for: 'X is a premiss of Y and a term of X is a minor term of Y'.

D 27. 'X is a mode of the first figure' for: 'X is a CS and the subject of the major premiss of X and the predicate of the minor premiss of X are middle terms of X'.

D 28. 'X is a mode of the second figure' for: 'X is a CS and the predicates of both premisses of X are middle terms of X'.

D 29. 'X is a mode of the third figure' for: 'X is a CS and the subjects of both premisses of X are middle terms of X'.

D 30. 'X is a mode of the fourth figure' for: 'X is a CS and the predicate of the major premiss of X and the subject of the minor premiss of X are middle terms of X'.

We shall also use the well known mnemotechnical names '*Barbara*', '*Celarent*' etc., But, as they are relevant only in metalogical, not in logical development of the theory of CS, we do not need to define them here.[2] It should be noted, however, that, starting with our definitions, the traditional metalogical system of CS could easily be constructed; we have done it elsewhere.[3]

---

[1] There are, therefore, *two* major terms in a CS, as also two minor and two middle terms. As a matter of fact, both have the same form (e.g. 'm' and 'm') but they are evidently *two* different terms, as they occupy different places in space. The talk about 'the same' term is caused by a confusion of the terms with the meaning of the terms; the latter is, evidently, identical in both cases.

[2] Cf. J. N. Keynes, *Studies and Exercises in Formal Logic*, 4th ed., London 1906. This is by far the best text-book of non-mathematical formal logic.

[3] I. M. Bocheński, *Zespol definicji do metalogicznego wykladu sylogistyki tradycyjnej* (Polish = A set of definitions for a metalogical development of traditional syllogistics), Polski Przegląd Tomistyczny, 1, 1939, 104–113.

2. Rules and method of deduction

We shall use two rules of substitution, a rule of definition and a rule of derivation. In order to be able to state rigorously the first two we must define 'substitution':

D 31. 'X is a substitution of Y for Z in T' for: 'X has the same form as T, except that everywhere, where a letter of the form of Z appears in T, a formula of the form of Y appears in X'. E.g. '$CAbmq$' is a substitution of 'Abm' for 'p' in 'Cpq'.

First rule of substitution: If X is a law of the system, a substitution of a proposition for a propositional variable contained in X is a law of the system.

Second rule of substitution: If X is a law of the system, a substitution of a nominal variable for a nominal variable contained in X is a law of the system. This rule enables us to change the lettering of 'a', 'b' and 'm'.

In order to state the rule of definition we shall first define 'definition':

D 32. 'Definition' for: 'formula composed of a proposition, of the symbol '$=$' and of another proposition'.

D 33. 'X is defined by Y' for: 'there is a definition such, that two propositions of the form of X and Y are united in it by '$=$' in whatever order'.

Rule of definition: If X is a law of the system, and Y is a part of X, and there is a definition such that Z is defined by Y in it – a substitution of Z for Y in X is a law of the system.

Rule of derivation: If an implication is a law of the system, and a proposition of the form of its antecedent is a law of the system, then a proposition of the form of its consequent is a law of the system.

The technique of the deduction will be the following:

Before each law to be proved, a 'probativeverse' will be written. This verse will be always composed of two parts, united by an '$=$', of which each indicates the same formula in a different way. The left part will always start with a number of the law (of the theory of propositions) which is assumed as a basis. Then the following indications will be given:

1. When applying the laws of substitution: a letter of the form of the letter to be substituted, followed by an '$/$', followed by the letter which has to be put in its place. E.g. suppose that we have

(1) Cpp

and wish to prove '$CAbaAba$'. We shall write:

$$(1)\, p/Aba = (2)$$

20

(2) *CAbaAba*

The probative verse is to be read: 'take (*1*); apply the rule of substitution, putting '*Aba*' for '*p*' in (*1*); you will obtain (*2*)'.

2. If the rule of definition is applied, the number of the law used as a basis will be followed by an '×' followed by the number of the definition needed. E.g. if we have the definition

(*1*) *Oba* = *NAba*

and the law

(*2*) *CObaOba*

in order to obtain '*CObaNAba*' we write:

$$(2) \times (1) \, II^\circ = (3)$$

(*3*) *CObaNAba*

The '*II°*' means that the definition has to be applied in the second occurrence of '*Oba*' only.

3. The application of the rule of derivation is indicated by writing on the right side of the probative verse the same implication, which is already indicated by the left side, but with an explicit statement of the laws used as antecedents. E.g. if we have

(*1*) *CpCqr*

(*2*) *p*

and we wish to prove '*Cqr*', we shall write:

$$(1) = \mathrm{C}(2) - (3)$$

(*3*) *Cqr*

'*C*(2) − (3)' means exactly the same thing as '(*1*)', namely '*CpCqr*', but it indicates (by the '*C*' and the figures) how the rule of derivation has to be applied.

Several rules will often be used together in the same demonstration. Thus the number of the definition used will be often followed by the indication of substitutions, etc.

3. Definitions and axioms

We are going to use two definitions only (*1* and *2*), but sixteen axioms, divided into two groups. The first group (*3–14*) consists of laws of the general theory of deduction, or logic of (unexplained) propositions, corresponding to the Scholastic *consequentiae*. The second, composed of four axioms (*15–18*) contains specific principles of our theory. Here are the definitions and axioms:

1.	$Eba = NIba$	*10.*	$CCKpqrCpCqr$
2.	$Oba = NAba$	*11.*	$CCKpqrCqCpr$
3.	Cpp	*12.*	$CCKpqrCCsqCKpsr$
4.	$CCpNqCqNp$	*13.*	$CCKpqrCKpNrNq$
5.	$CCpqCNqNp$	*14.*	$CCKpqrCKqpr$
6.	$CCpqCCqrCpr$	*15.*	Aaa
7.	$CNNpp$	*16.*	Iaa
8.	$CCKpqrCKNrqNp$	*17.*	$CKAmaAbmAba$
9.	$CCKpqrCCspCKsqr$	*18.*	$CKEmaIbmOba$

It will be useful to give at once an interpretation of these formulae. *1* and *2* are definitions, i.e. abbreviations without any importance, except for practical means; the system could have been developed without them. *3* is a form of the principle of identity: 'if *p*, then *p*'. *5* is the law of simple contraposition, explicitly stated by Aristotle [1] and well-known to the Scholastics;[2] it may be also considered as a form of the *modus tollendo tollens*. *4* is another form of *5*. *6* is the so-called 'principle of (hypothetical) syllogism' which is often formulated as follows: 'if *p*, then *q*; if *q*, then *r*; therefore: if *p*, then *r*'.[3] *7* is known as the principle of double negation: 'if not-not-*p*, then *p*'. *8* and *13* are the two laws on which the indirect reduction of CS's is based, namely *8* is used when the negation of the conclusion is to be substituted for the major premiss, *13* when for the minor. The corresponding principle was formulated by Aristotle,[4] and the Scholastics had an analogous rule.[5] *9* and *12* are again the two laws on which the direct reduction is founded, *9* serving when the major, *12* when the minor is to be converted. This principle is continuously used both by Aristotle and the Scholastics, but we have not found it explicitly formulated; nor do the *Principia* contain it. *10* and *11* are the so-called 'laws of exportation', which allow us to transform a product into an implication; they are needed for purely technical reasons, as without them we would need some more rules. Finally, the last axiom taken from the logic of propositions is *14*, which allows us to change the order of the

---

[1] *An. Priora* B *4, 57 b* pp, 1 f.
[2] Cf. I. M. Bocheński, *De consequentiis Scholasticorum earumque origine*, Angelicum 15, 1938 (pp. 92–109), p. 9, N. 6.
[3] *Ibid.* p. 9, N. 4.
[4] *An Priora* B *4, 57 a* pp. 36 f.
[5] Cf. *De consequentiis...* p. 9, N. 7 and p. 10, N. 9.

premisses, an operation needed in traditional doctrine whenever the mnemotechnic name of a mode contains an '*m*'.

The remaining four axioms are specific and belong to the theory of CS as such. *15* means, according to our interpretation, 'all *a*'s are *a*'s'; it is, consequently, just a form of the principle of identity. *16* means 'some *a*'s are *a*'s'; it looks like a curiously weakened form of the same principle; but, as we shall see, its importance is capital. *17* is the well known *Barbara,* *18* the *Ferio.* Thus our system starts from evident laws of the general theory of propositions and from four special axioms of which three at least possess a very high grade of intuitive evidence; the same will probably be said by the majority of the readers about *16*: for, if all *a*'s are *a*'s, it seems that, *a fortiori*, some *a*'s are *a*'s. This is, however, a hotly disputed point, with which we shall deal later on. But a reader who does not know the complicated problems of recent logic will surely feel that we are starting from perfectly clear and evident axioms.

4. Deduction

We proceed now to the deduction of the laws of contradiction:

$$3 \, p/Eba \times 1 \, II° = 20$$

20. *CEbaNIba*

$$3 \, p/NIba \times 1 \, II° = 21$$

21. *CNIbaEba*

$$4 \, p/Eba, q/Iba = C20 - 22$$

22. *CIbaNEba*

$$5 \, p/NIba, q/Eba = C21 - (1)$$

  (*1*) *CNEbaNNIba*

$$6 \, p/NEba, q/NNIba, r/Iba = C(1) - C7 \, p/Iba - 23$$

23. *CNEbaIba*

$$3 \, p/Oba \times 2 \, II° = 24$$

24. *CObaNAba*

$$3 \, p/Oba \times 2 \, I° = 25$$

25. *CNAbaOba*

$$4 \, p/Oba, q/Aba = C24 - 26$$

26. *CAbaNOba*

$$5 \, p/NAba, q/Oba = C25 - (1)$$

  (*1*) *CNObaNNaba*

$$6 \, p/NOba, q/NNAba, r/Aba = C(1) - C7 \, p/Aba - 27$$

23

27. *CNObaAba*

In order to be able to deduce the other laws of the logical square and those of conversion we must first obtain *Datisi*:

$$8 \; p/Eba, \; q/Imb, \; r/Oma = C18 \; b/m, \; m/b - (1)$$

(*1*) *CKNOmaImbNEba*
$$9 \; p/NOma, \; q/Imb, \; r/NEba, \; s/Ama = C(1) - C26 \; b/m - (2)$$

(*2*) *CKAmaImbNEba*
$$6 \; p/KAmaImb, \; q/NEba, \; r/Iba = C(2) - C23 - 30$$

30. *CKAmaImbIba*   (Datisi)

From *30* we obtain first the law of conversion of *I* propositions, then the law of subalternation $A - I$; the law of conversion of *A* propositions follows from the two, as also the other laws of the logical square and of conversion.

$$10 \; p/Abb, \; q/Iba, \; r/Iab = C30 \; a/b, \; b/a, \; m/b - C15 \; a/b - 31$$

31. *CIbaIab*   (Law of conversion of *I* propositions)

$$11 \; p/Aba, \; q/Ibb, \; r/Iba = C30 \; m/b - C16 \; a/b - 32$$

32. *CAbaIba*   (Law of subalternation of $A - I$ propositions)

$$6 \; p/Aba, \; q/Iba, \; r/Iab = C32 - C31 - 33$$

33. *CAbaIab*   (Law of conversion of *A* propositions)

$$5 \; p/Iab, \; q/Iba \times 1 \times 1 \; a/b, \; b/a = C31 \; a/b, \; b/a - 34$$

34. *CEbaEab*   (Law of simple conversion of *E* propositions)

$$5 \; p/Aba, \; q/Iba \times 1 \times 2 = C32 - 35$$

35. *CEbaOba*   (Law of subalternation of $E - O$ propositions)

$$6 \; p/Eba, \; q/Eab, \; r/Oab = C34 - C35 \; a/b, \; b/a - 36$$

36. *CEbaOab*   (Law of conversion *per accidens* of *E* propositions)

$$5 \; p/Aba, \; q/Iba = C32 - 37$$

37. *CNIbaNAba*   (Second law of subalternation of $A - I$ propositions)

$$5 \; p/Eba, \; q/Oba = C35 - 38$$

38. *CNObaNEba*   (Second law of subalternation of $E - O$ propositions)

$6\ p/Aba,\ q/NOba,\ r/NEba = C26 - C38 - 39$

39. *CAbaNEba*   (First law of contrariety)

$6\ p/Eba,\ q/NIba,\ r/NAba = C20 - C37 - 40$

40. *CEbaNAba*   (Second law of contrariety)

$6\ p/NIba,\ q/NAba,\ r/Oba = C37 - C25 - 41$

41. *CNIbaOba*   (First law of subcontrariety)

$6\ p/NOba,\ q/NEba,\ r/Iba = C38 - C23 - 42$

42. *CNObaIba*   (Second law of subcontrariety)

Thus all laws of conversion and of the logical square have been demonstrated. We proceed now to the demonstration of the remaining four modes of the first figure – the *Barbara* (*17*) and the *Ferio* (*18*) being already in our system as axioms

$6\ p/KAmaAbm,\ q/Aba,\ r/Iba = C17 - C32 - 50$

50. *CKAmaAbmIba*   (Barbari)

$12\ p/Ama,\ q/Imb,\ r/Iba,\ s/Ibm = C30 - C31a/m - 51$

51. *CKAmaIbmIba*   (Darii)

In order to proceed further we must first obtain *Festino:*

$9\ p/Ema,\ q/Ibm,\ r/Oba,\ s/Eam = C18 - C34a/m,\ b/a - 52$

52. *CKEamIbmOba*   (Festino)

$13\ p/Ema,\ q/Iba,\ r/Obm \times 1 = C52a/m,\ m/a - (1)$

    (*1*)   *CKEmaNObmEba*

$12\ p/Ema,\ q/NObm,\ r/Eba,\ s/Abm = C(1) - C26a/m - 53$

53. *CKEmaAbmEba*   (Celarent)

$6\ p/KEmaAbm,\ q/Eba,\ r/Oba = C53 - C35 - 54$

54. *CKEmaAbmOba*   (Celaront)

The six modes of the first figure are thus all in our system. We shall now demonstrate the remaining five modes of the second figure (*Festino* having been proved above, *52*).

$13\ p/Aam,\ q/Aba,\ r/Abm \times 2a/m \times 2 = C17a/m,\ m/a - 55$

55. *CKAamObmOba*   (Baroco)

$9\ p/Ema,\ q/Abm,\ r/Eba,\ s/Eam = C53 - C34a/m,\ b/a - 56$

56. *CKEamAbmEba*   (Cesare)

$6\ p/KEamAbm,\ q/Eba,\ r/Oba = C56 - C35 - 57$

57. *CKEamAbmOba*   (Cesaro)

$14\ p/Ema,\ q/Abm,\ r/Eba = C53 - (1)$

(1) *CKAbmEmaEba*
 12 p/Aam, q/Emb, r/Eab, s/Ebm
 $= C(1)a/b, b/a — C34a/m — (2)$

(2) *CKAamEbmEab*
 6 p/KAamEbm, q/Eab, r/Eba = C(2) — C34a/b, b/a — 58

58. *CKAamEbmEba*   (Camestres)
 6 p/KAamEbm, q/Eba, r/Oba = C58 — C35 — 59

59. *CKAamEbmOba*   (Camestrop)

Having demonstrated all modes of the second figure, we proceed to the demonstration of the modes of the third; *Datisi*, however, has been proved above (*30*), so that we need to prove only five modes.

 8 p/Aba, q/Amb, r/Ama × 2b/m × 2 = C17b/m, m/b — 60

60. *CKOmaAmbOba*   (Bocardo)
 14 p/Amb, q/Ima, r/Iab = C30a/b, b/a — (1)

(1) *CKImaAmbIab*
 6 p/KImaAmb, q/Iab, r/Iba = C(1) — C31a/b, b/a — 61

61. *CKImaAmbIba*   (Disamis)
 12 p/Ama, q/Imb, r/Iba, s/Amb = C30 — C32a/b, b/m — 62

62. *CKAmaAmbIba*   (Darapti)
 12 p/Ema, q/Ibm, r/Oba, s/Imb = C18 — C31a/b, b/m — 63

63. *CKEmaImbOba*   (Ferison)
 12 p/Ema, q/Ibm, r/Oba, s/Amb = C18 — C33a/b, b/m — 64

64. *CKEmaAmbOba*   (Felapton)

The six modes of the fourth figure will be demonstrated now.
 12 p/Eam, q/Ibm, r/Oba, s/Imb = C52 — C31a/b, b/m — 65

65. *CKEamImbOba*   (Fresison)
 12 p/Eam, q/Ibm, r/Oba, s/Amb = C52 — C33a/b, b/m — 66

66. *CKEamAmbOba*   (Fesapo)
 9 p/Ima, q/Amb, r/Iba, s/Iam = C61 — C31a/m, b/a — 67

67. *CKIamAmbIba*   (Dimaris)
 9 p/Ima, q/Amb, r/Iba, s/Aam = C61 — C33 a/m, b/a — 68

68. *CKAamAmbIba*   (Bamalip)
 12 p/Aam, q/Ebm, r/Eba, s/Emb = C58 — C34 a/b, b/m — 69

69. *CKAamEmbEba*   (Camenes)
 6 p/KAamEmb, q/Eba, r/Oba = C69 — C35 — 70

70. *CKAamEmbOba*   (Camenop)

5. Partial and alternative systems

We are now going to investigate what in our system depends on each of the axioms and how these axioms could be replaced by others, i.e. we shall discuss some partial and alternative systems. Every conclusion of this chapter can easily be proved rigorously; but because of lack of space we shall give our proofs according to the method commonly used by mathematicians, i.e. we shall limit ourselves to sketches of proofs.

The system developed above will be called 'T system'. It contains, as has been shown, the laws of the logical square, the laws of simple and *per accidens* conversion, and twenty-four modes. These modes may be usefully ordered in the following table:[1]

Line	First figure	Second figure	Third figure
1.	Barbara (17)	Baroco (55)	Bocardo (60)
2.	Barbari (50)	Camestrop (59)	Felapton (64)
3.	Darii (51)	Camestres (58)	Ferison (63)
4.	Celarent (53)	Festino (52)	Disamis (61)
5.	Celaront (54)	Cesaro (57)	Darapti (62)
6.	Ferio (18)	Cesare (56)	Datisi (30)
		Fourth figure	
7.	Dimaris (67)	Camenes (69)	Fresison (65)
8.	Bamalip (68)	Camenop (70)	Fesapo (66)

All modes in the same horizontal line may be deduced one from the other by means of *8* or *13*. Further, the modes of line 2 may be deduced from those immediately over them in line 1, or from those immediately under them in line 3, by use of *6*, *9* or *12* with some of the laws of subalternation. The same is true of the modes of line 5, which may be deduced from those of the fourth or sixth line. Finally, the same method may be applied to the modes of line 8 by deducing them from the modes of line 7.

---

[1] The table was stated by J. N. Keynes, *Studies and Exercises in Formal Logic*, London 1884 (the 4th ed., 1906 was used, pp. 334 f.), but its essentials are a discovery of Leibniz, cf. L. Couturat, *La Logique de Leibniz*, Paris 1901, p. 16. It is, however, highly probable that the Scholastics (about whose Logic we know practically nothing) had already a corresponding scheme, as the main methods were established by Aristotle himself in *An. Priora B*.

These remarks will help make clear the following considerations about partial systems. Four such systems are obtained by dropping one of our axioms *15—18*:

(1) *System NA*, without *15* ('*Aaa*'). *31* cannot be proved and therefore, *33, 34* and *36* are dropped. Thus all laws of conversion become invalid, while the laws of the logical square remain intact. Many of our proofs of the modes are now illegitimate; but by devising new methods we may still prove twelve modes. As the proofs of *30, 55, 56* and *60* remain valid, the modes of the second line in our table can be proved by those of the first, using *32* and *35*. Also the modes of line 5 are inferred from those of line 6. We have together four lines, i.e. twelve modes.

(2) *System NI*, without *16* ('*Iaa*'). *32* cannot be proved and therefore all laws of the logical square, except those of contradiction (*20–27*), as also the laws of conversion *per accidens* (*33* and *36*) become illegitimate. Out of the modes, nine are now incorrect, namely *Barbari* (*50*), *Celaront* (*54*), *Cesaro* (*57*), *Camestrop* (*59*), *Darapti* (*62*), *Felapton* (*64*), *Fesapo* (*66*), *Bamalip* (*68*) and *Camenop* (*70*). The proofs of some other modes also become illegitimate, but they can be replaced by new ones, on the same lines as above. We know, however, of no valid proof for the nine modes mentioned. We are left with fifteen modes (lines 1, 3, 4, 6 and 7).

(3) *System NB*, without *17* (*Barbara*). Only three modes are lost, namely those of the first line; the modes of the second line are now proved by those of the third. The system contains, consequently, all laws of conversion and of the logical square with twenty-one modes. Curiously enough, the omission of *Barbara* does not affect the system as the omission of other axioms does.[1]

(4) *System NF*, without *18* (*Ferio*). *30* (*Datisi*) cannot be proved and, consequently, all laws of conversion and of the logical square are dropped, except those of contradiction. Out of the modes, three only can be inferred, namely those of the first line. All that remains from the system are the laws of contradiction, *Barbara*, *Baroco* and *Bocardo*.

It is to be noticed that these partial systems are true parts of the *T* system, i.e. that the addition of one axiom converts each of them into the full *T* system, while the part depending on each axiom is clearly determined.

---

[1] The omission of *Barbara*, however, is in one respect very important: no *Sorites* can be constructed in a system like that (this observation was made by I. Thomas).

This is very important, for it shows that, if there is no contradiction in the *T* system, there can be no contradiction between our five systems.

A specially interesting case is that of the relation of the *NI* and *T* systems. The *NI* system is a part of the *T* system; but by the omission of our *16* the nature of the operator '*I*' is deeply affected. Namely, in the *NI* system '*I*' may be defined as a bi-valued truth-operator; in the *T* system it cannot.[1]

The situation is, consequently, similar to that which arises when we drop the last of the twelve axioms of the classical bi-valued logic of propositions, as stated by Professor Łukasiewicz [2]: we obtain then the system of Professor Heyting [3], which is not a bi-valued truth-system.

Here is a sketch of a proof of our assertion. It is easy to see that our '*A*' operator can be defined (in bi-valued logic) only by the truth-table *1011*, i.e. by the truth-table of implication.[4] Now in our *T* system '*I*' is (1) reflexive (because of *16*), (2) symmetric (because of *31*) and (3) not transitive (as '*CKImaIbmIba*' is not a law of the system). Let us suppose it is a bi-valued truth-operator. If so, its truth-table must be one of the following four: (1) *1111*, (2) *1101*, (3) *1011*, (4) *1001*, as those are the only truth-tables of reflexive operators.[5] Now it is evidently not (1), as in that case

---

[1] The following considerations may appear difficult for a reader who is not initiated into mathematical logic; he may omit them. If, however, he would wish to read these lines, the following explanations will perhaps be useful. By 'value' (in bi-valued logic) the truth or the falsehood of a proposition is meant, the truth being symbolised by '*1*', the falsehood by '*0*'. A truth-value-operator (short: 'truth operator') is an operator which can be defined by truth-value-tables (also called 'truth-tables') alone. What a truth-table is, may be seen from the following instance. The conjunction ('*Kpq*') is defined by the truth-table:

'if the value of '*p*' is   *1 1 0 0*
and the value of '*q*' is   *1 0 1 0*
then the value of '*Kpq*' is *1 0 0 0*'

The last line may be given alone as a definition of a truth-operator.

[2] J. Łukasiewicz, *Die Logik und das Grundlagenproblem*, ex.: F. Gonseth, *Les entretiens*, Zürich 1941, 82–100, espec. pp. 86f.

[3] A. Heyting, *Die formalen Regeln der intuitionistischen Logik*, Sitzb. d. Preuss. Ak. d. Wiss., Phys. Math. Kl., 1930, 42–56.

[4] This, however, would imply '*0*' to become transitive as well by definition (1), contrary to the classic theory (remark of the editor).

[5] All these four truth-operators are transitive and for that reason alone must be dropped (remark of the editor).

each substitution of '*Iba*' would be a true proposition. It is also not (4), this being the truth-table of equivalence which is transitive, while '*I*' is not. Neither can it be (2), because of *32* which would have the value *0* if we put *a/1, b/0*. Thus we are left with (3). But (3) has been shown to be the truth-table of '*A*' and if this be also the truth-table of '*I*', both operators would be equivalent and the system quite trivial. It appears, consequently, that '*I*' is not a truth operator in the *T* system. Consequently the *T* system cannot be considered as a bi-valued truth-system.

But if we drop *16*, '*I*' is no more reflexive. It is easy to find now among the sixteen truth-tables of bi-valued logic one which satisfies all axioms: this is namely *1110*, i.e. the truth-table of the alternative. Thus the *NI* system can be interpreted as a bi-valued truth-system.[1]

Many alternative systems of axioms fulfilling all[2] conditions needed to obtain the full system *T* may be chosen. Here are some of these possible sets:

(1) *31, 16, 17, 18*. The law of conversion of *I* propositions may be substituted for our '*Aaa*'.

(2) *15, 32, 17, 18*. The law of subalternation of *A* — *I* propositions may be chosen instead of our '*Iaa*'.

(3) *15, 16, 55, 18* or *15, 16, 60, 18*.

(4) *15, 16, 17, 30* or *15, 16, 17, 56*. The former was chosen by Professor Lukasiewicz, as it allows a simple course of deduction.

(5) *31, 16, 17, 53: Celarent* instead of *Ferio*. This is indeed the method recommended (as far as *17* and *53* are concerned) by Aristotle himself; it has the advantage of the perfect intuitiveness of *53*. In that case *61* is proved first by *8*, then from *61* and *10*, putting *m/a*, we obtain *32*; thus, as *31* is an axiom here, all the remaining laws are easily inferred.

(6) *31, 32, 17, 53*, i.e. the laws of conversion of *I* and of subalternation of *A* — *I* propositions, *Barbara* and *Celarent*. This would be a system most conformed to the traditional way. But *15* and, above all, *16* have great advantages because of their simplicity and as they allow one to see on what some questioned laws depend.

---

[1] The definitions (1) and (2), however, result in '*E*' and '*O*' becoming transitive (remark of the editor).

[2] In the systems (1) and (5), however, 15 is not deducible and in (6) both, 15 and 16, are not deducible. This was shown by Ivo Thomas. – This, however, is of no great importance since both propositions are not originally a part of classic syllogistic (for the first time they were used by Leibniz); (remark of the editor).

6. Unsolved problems

We are terminating our formal analysis of the theory of CS by the enumeration of some logical problems which have not yet been solved and need to be investigated. [1]

(1) Is the '*I*' operator in our *T* system a truth-operator, and if so, of a logic of how many values? [2]

(2) Is there any connection between the traditional doctrine of CS (i.e. our *T* system) and the intuitionistic logic of Professor Brouwer? There are some reasons to believe that it may be so. Namely (i) we have shown that it is not a bi-valued system; (ii) it has been proved that a set of traditional, very intuitive rules of deduction gives rise not to the classical bi-valued logic of propositions, but to an intuitionistic system. Now there is a striking similarity between the intuitiveness of these rules and that of our axioms.

(3) Is the *T* system a non-contradictory one? This is a very important, indeed the most important problem of every logical system.

(4) Is it complete? There can be, of course, no question of asserting that the laws inferred here are all the laws of the system. But two questions

[1] Most of those problems have been solved since the publication of this article – a very good example for the progress made in formal logic. J. C. Shepherdson (*On the interpretation of Aristotelian syllogistic*, Journal of Symbolic Logic 21, 1956, 137–147) has solved problem (1): The '*I*' operator is *no* truth-operator. The following have proved that the system is non-contradictory, respectively complete, that is to say they have solved problems (3) and (4): J. Słupecki (*Z badań nad sylogistyką Arystotelesa*, Trav. de la Soc. d. Sciences et d. Lettres de Wrocław, sér. B 9, pp. 187–191; *On Aristotelian syllogistic*, Studia Philosophica 4, Poznań 1949/50, 275–300), A. Wedberg (*The Aristotelian Theory of Classes*, Ajatus 15, 1948, 299–314), A. Menne (*Logik und Existenz*, Meisenheim 1954, pp. 61f.). This last-mentioned book also shows that none of the syllogistic operators can be a truth-operator, that, on the contrary, the classic system is part of the class calculus, that is to say, of the so-called definite class calculus in which null- and universal class are excluded. Herewith problem (2) has been solved as well in a way that CS remains within the sphere of bi-valued logic as the definite class calculus is based upon the bi-valued propositional calculus. Finally, Ivo Thomas shows that one basic term and three special axioms the independence of which, problem (5), Menne shows op. cit. p. 62, are sufficient for appropriate definitions. Menne needs ten theorems of the propositional calculus only instead of twelve used by Bocheński and Thomas.

[2] By introducing other values than *1* and *0*, Łukasiewicz and Post obtained more-valued (e.g. three-valued) logics. For an exhaustive account of such theories cf. R. Feys, *Les Logiques nouvelles de la modalité*, Revue Néoscolastique de Philosophie, 40, 1937, 517–553; 41, 1938, 217–252.

may be examined: (i) can it be proved that every law which cannot be deduced from the axioms of the T system is a negation of some of its laws? (ii) can it be proved, that the only laws of the form '$CKXxyYztZuv$' which may be deduced from the axioms of the T system are those enumerated above and their substitutions?

(5) Are the axioms independent?

It is the belief of the writer that Thomistic philosophers would do better to examine these and similar problems than to occupy themselves with some more or less 'existentialistic' theories which might perhaps be left rather to poets and other masters of imagination.

II. DISCUSSION OF SOME PHILOSOPHICAL PROBLEMS

Having secured a rigorous basis, we may proceed now to the examination of several philosophical problems connected with CS. This examination will be achieved in an informal way; we shall try, however, to keep at least to the traditional Scholastic level of exactness which is a middle way between formal rigour and the bad poetical method used by most contemporary philosophers. There will be three chapters: (1) On method in the theory of CS, (2) On the importance of CS, (3) On the so-called problem of the null-class.

1. On method in the theory of CS

Thesis 1. Formalism should be applied to the theory of CS

Explanation. By 'formalism' a method is meant, according to which we first make a choice of terms with strictly determined meanings, then abstract from their meaning and develop the system as if it were a mere aggregate of heaps of dry ink on paper; finally, having reached the conclusions, we reinterpret our symbols.

Opinions. While all recent (mathematical) logicians continuously apply formalism to all systems of logic, all irrationalists and many idealists (as B. Croce)[1] reject any use of it. Curiously enough, many eminent Thomists are following the irrationalists (as J. Maritain).[2]

---

[1] The *Logica* of B. Croce is even one of the best instances of this position. It also gives abundant evidence as to the fact that this 'logic' (exactly as similar 'logics' of Hegel and other 'logicians') is no logic at all; the name is abusively used.

[2] This seems at least to be the position of the celebrated philosopher in J. Maritain,

Proof. The method which leads to the easiest, most rigorous and most secure development of the theory of CS should be applied to the theory of CS; but formalism is this method; Thesis.

The major is evident; the minor is justified by historical induction. As a matter of fact, formalism, which is one of the greatest inventions of Aristotle, has been the cause of considerable progress in formal logic, whenever it has been applied, e.g. by the Stoics, the Scholastics and the mathematical logicians [1]; but the theory of CS is a part of formal logic.

Objection. A method which supposes that the subject-matter of logic is heaps of dry ink, should not be applied to the theory of CS; but formalism is such method; Antithesis.

The major is a corollary of the Thomistic theory, according to which the subject-matter of logic is *ens rationis*; the minor follows from the above description of formalism.

Answer. Conceding the major we deny the minor and the conclusion. As a matter of fact, one who applies formalism does not assume any position as to the problem of the subject-matter of logic. For, the symbols he uses, even if he temporarily abstracts from their meaning for the sake of utility, are supposed to mean something; if they did not mean anything, one could hardly see any use in studying logic. Now what is meant by specifically logical symbols (as negations, quantifiers, implica-

---

Eléments de Philosophie, II, L'ordre des concepts, I. Petite Logique, 5th. ed., Paris 1923, pp. 263–279, especially pp. 275f. But we cannot be sure of it, because of the vagueness of J. Maritain's style.

[1] If this fact is often ignored, it is due to the influence of K. Prantl, *Geschichte derLogik im Abendlande,* repr. Berlin 1927. The author knows practically everything about the subject and, at the same time, hardly understands anything about formal logic. He hates the Stoics and Scholastics; the philosophy of St. Thomas Aquinas is to him just an 'unverständliche Verquickung' due to an 'unklaren Verstand' (III, 108); the magnificent development of Stoic logic is a 'grenzenlose Stupidität' (III, 474) etc. Recent research into the history of formal logic, made by mathematical logicians has completely changed the outlook. Cf. H. Scholz, *Geschichte der Logik,* Berlin 1931; J. Łukasiewicz, *Zur Geschichte der Aussagenlogik,* Erkenntnis 5, 1935/6, 111–131; E. W. Beth, *Geschiedenis der Logica,* Den Haag, 1944. A good historical introduction is contained in R. Feys, *Logistiek,* I. Antwerpen 1944; see also I. M. Bocheński, *Notiones historiae logicae formalis,* Angelicum 13, 1936, 109–123; *Notes historiques sur les propositions modales,* Rev. d. Sc. Phil. et Theol. 26, 1937, 673–692. The standard book for the history of Logic is now: I. M. Bocheński, *Formale Logik* (history of problems), Freiburg i. Br., 1956. An English translation is being prepared by Ivo Thomas.

tions etc.), is according to the Thomistic theory *ens rationis,* while the nominalists contend that their meaning is purely syntactical, and the Platonist would hold that they are some subsistent entities. Formalism may be used by all of them and has nothing to do with any position.

Thesis 2. No tacit assumption should be deliberately admitted in a system of CS

This follows from Thesis 1. For, once formalism is applied, i.e. once we limit our attention to the external form of the symbols, we can no more deal with tacit assumptions. But there are also other serious reasons for upholding the thesis. Namely, tacit assumptions are generally unanalysed assumptions, i.e. they may be false. Also, the whole business of formal logic is to make the tacit assumptions of reasoning explicit. To deny the thesis would be, consequently, to contradict the very nature of formal logic, not only as it is now, but as it has always been since the time of Aristotle.

Corollary. The so-called 'indirect first figure'[1] should not be recognized in the theory of CS. As a matter of fact, the theory of this figure supposes that we know, without specifying how, which term has the largest denotation and which the smallest; it is thus based on a tacit assumption. The theory of the fourth figure does not make any such assumption, as it defines the major and minor term by their formal position in the CS.

Thesis 3. No metaphysical assumptions should be used in a theory of CS.

Opinions. While old Scholastics and contemporary formal logicians hold the thesis, some recent Thomists believe that one cannot develop formal logic without some metaphysical assumptions. This is the opinion among others, of J. Maritain.[2]

---

[1] As to the history of that figure cf. F. Solmsen, *Die Entwicklung der Aristotelischen Logik und Rhetorik,* Berlin 1929, where it is shown how that figure and the assumptions on which it is based were developed by Aristotle from the Platonic *diairesis.* Cf. Also J. W. Stakelum, C. M., *Galen and the Logic of Propositions,* Rome 1940; I. M. Bocheński, *La logique de Théophraste,* 2nd ed. Fribourg 1947. Fr. Stakelum has proved that the fourth figure is not a 'Galenic' figure.

[2] J. Maritain, *op. cit.* p. 269. Maritain affirms that the problem of existential import cannot be solved without introducing considerations about the matter of propositions, i.e. without metaphysical assumptions. Now the problem of existential import is a problem of formal logic, for its solutions affect the validity of some laws of formal logic. Thus Maritain seems to think, that formal logic cannot be developed without some metaphysical assumptions.

Proof. No assumption, belonging to a theory which itself uses CSs, should be used in a theory of CS; but metaphysical assumptions are such; Thesis. The major is a form of the principle which prohibits the vicious circle reasoning; the minor may be proved by inspecting any book of Thomistic metaphysics, where CSs are continuously in use. Thesis 3 seems to be traditional in Thomism: the so-called 'minor' i.e. formal logic has always been developed at the beginning of each treatise of philosophy without any metaphysical assumptions.

2. On the importance of CS

Thesis 4. The theory of CS is not the whole but a proper part of formal logic

Explanation. The thesis means that there are laws of formal logic which (1) are not CS's nor laws of conversion or of the logical square and (2) cannot be deduced from any set of such laws.

Opinions. While the Old Scholastics implicitly acknowledged the theses[1], many modern Thomistic thinkers deny it; they sometimes even try to prove that all non-syllogistic laws of formal logic may be deduced from the theory of CS.[2] Mathematical logicians explicitly uphold the thesis.

Proof. If there are laws of formal logic which (1) are not CSs nor laws either of conversion or of the logical square and (2) cannot be deduced from any set of such laws – the theory of CS is not the whole but a proper part of formal logic; but it is so; Thesis.

The major is evident; the minor is proved as follows: (1) Laws of the logic of propositions (e.g. the *modus ponendo ponens*) and many others are laws of formal logic; but they are neither CSs, nor laws of conversion, nor laws of the logical square. (2) Laws of a completely different nature from these laws cannot be deduced from them; but there are

---

[1] Old Scholastics had in their treatises of formal logic at least three distinct parts: (1) the *consequentiae,* (2) the syllogistic (assertoric *and* modal) (3) the *loci.* No attempt was made, as far as we know, to 'reduce' the first or the third to the second. Cf. our *De consequentiis* quoted above (footnote 2 on page 22 and also I. M. Bocheński, *S. Thomae Aquinatis De Modalibus opusculum et doctrina,* Angelicum 17,1940 180–218.
[2] Cf. the 'reduction' in J. Gredt, O.S.B., *Elementa Philosophiae Aristotelico-Thomisticae,* 4th ed., Freiburg i.Br. 1926, pp. 67f. This is perhaps the best of our textbooks; and yet the confusions it contains are almost incredible. Generally speaking, the level of Thomistic textbooks of logic is now very low, far lower than it was in the 13th century.

many such laws, e.g. the laws of logic of propositions. The last minor is easily proved by the fact that, while the formulae of the theory of CS contain only nominal variables, the laws of the logic of propositions contain only propositional variables. Similar proofs may be given for other kinds of laws.

Corollary. It is urgent that the traditional treatises of the *consequentiae* and of the *loci,* which deal with non-syllogistic laws, should be re-introduced into contemporary Thomistic textbooks of logic.

Thesis 5. The question: 'Is the CS an important part of logic?' is a pseudo-problem

Proof. All questions postulating an absolute attribution of a relative predicate are pseudo-problems; but the question 'Is the CS an important part of logic?' is such; Thesis.

The major is evident: such questions are meaningless and can have no answer. The minor: CS may be important (1) for the system of formal logic as a whole, (2) for practical use, and then again: (a) in metaphysics, (b) in empirical science; it may also be important for one of these aims and unimportant for another. In order that the question might be answered it must be specified for what CS is thought to be important.

Thesis 6. The CS is an important tool for metaphysics

This is proved by the use all metaphysicians, both old and new, are constantly making of CS's; Professor Hartmann [1] is an instance. On the other side it seems that CS is far less important for empirical science. This explains why logical positivists, who are only interested in methods of the empirical sciences, deny the importance of CS, while metaphysicians affirm it.

Thesis 7. The CS is not the only logical tool needed in metaphysics

The thesis has been proved by an exact formal analysis of two demonstrations of St. Thomas Aquinas.[2] Nobody who has ever read these analyses

---

[1] Cf. N. Hartmann, *Zur Grundlegung der Ontologie,* Berlin 1935 and other writings by the same author.

[2] J. Salamucha, *Dowod 'ex motu' na istnienie Boga* (Polish = Demonstration from movement of the existence of God), Collectanea Theologica, Lwów, 15, 1934, 53–92; I. M. Bocheński, *Nove Lezioni di Logica Simbolica,* Roma 1938, pp. 147–155 (Analysis of the Thomistic proof of immortality of the human soul).

36

can doubt that other laws than CS's are used by this great thinker and that it is absurd to try to analyse them by means of CSs only.

Corollary. It is urgent that Thomists should learn recent mathematical logic and apply it in their analyses of Thomistic proofs and in systematic demonstrations.

3. On the so-called problem of the null-class

Thesis 8. The traditional theory of CS contains no errors

Opinions. Some medieval logicians believed that many laws of our T system, namely all those which are not conained in the NI system, are erroneous [1]; the same has been believed by many mathematical logicians who asserted that the traditional doctrine of CS, because it ignores the null class (a class without elements), contains errors. Recent mathematical logicians [2] and Thomists admit the thesis.

Proof. No system which (1) is strictly formally developed and which (2) does not lead to false propositions, contains errors; but the traditional theory of CS is such system; Thesis.

The major is evident. The minor is justified: (1) by our formal system which is identical with the traditional theory of CS, (2) by the principle *quod gratis affirmatur, gratis negatur,* for it has never been proved that our system gives rise to false propositions. Thus the argument is sufficient to establish our thesis dialectically; a rigorous proof would, however, require a demonstration of non-contradiction of the T system. [3]

Objection. All systems which contain some laws which lead, by correct substitutions, to false propositions, contain errors; but the theory of CS is such; Antithesis.

The major is evident. The minor is proved as follows. Take our *33* and

---

[1] At least this seems to follow from the fact that John of St. Thomas discusses that position. Cf. Ioannis a S. Thoma, *Cursus Philosophicus* I, ed. P. B. Reiser, O.S.B., Taurini 1930, pp. 32f.

[2] E.g. D. Hilbert und W. Ackermann, *Grundzüge der theoretischen Logik,* Berlin 1928, p. 41: 'Diese Diskrepanz rührt davon her, dass die seit Aristoteles traditionell gewordene Deutung der positiven allgemeinen Sätze ('Alle *A* sind *B*') mit unserer Interpretation der Formeln (not-X v Y) nicht vollkommen in Einklang steht.' There is, consequently, no question of errors, but of differences of interpretation. That position seems to be common to-day, except with less important and unoriginal writers on logic, as e.g. M. Boll, *Eléments de Logique Scientifique,* Paris 1942 (a book as bad from the formal point of view as it is sectarian in its philosophical affirmations).

[3] The non-contradiction of CS has meanwhile been proved. See footnote 3 on page 30.

put 'wives of Copernicus' for '*b*', 'women' for '*a*'. We obtain by correct substitution 'If all wives of Copernicus are women, some women are wives of Copernicus.' The antecedent is true, but the consequent is false, as Copernicus has never been married and there are no women who are his wives. But a conditional proposition whose antecedent is true and whose consequent is false, is false, and this is a conditional proposition. Thus it is a false proposition.

Answer. We distinguish the major: all systems which contain laws which lead... any interpretation of the terms being given – we concede; all systems ... only if a certain interpretation of the terms is admitted, but not if another is given – we deny; we contradistinguish the minor and deny the conclusion.

Explanation. The interpretation needed for the correctness of the objection is that an *A* proposition has no existential import, while an *I* proposition has an existential import. But this is not the unique possible interpretation. In our system e.g. we assumed (by *16*) that every proposition, both *A* and *I*, has an existential import. Now, once such interpretation is assumed, the system does not give rise to any false proposition, as can be seen in all instances, e.g. in our above proposition about the wives of Copernicus. Thus the objection becomes invalid; it rests on an intolerant assumption that only one system is possible, namely our *NI* system.

Thesis 9. The system of CS upheld by the Peano-Russellian logic contains no errors

Explanation. Most of the contemporary mathematical logicians follow the system of Peano as developed by Professor Whitehead and Earl Russell; a part of this system is our *NI* system. As this does not contain some of the traditional laws, it has been said sometimes that the Peano-Russellian logic contains errors.

Proof: analogous to the proof of Thesis 8.

Corollary. It is necessary to distinguish the current Peano-Russellian system from mathematical logic as a whole. E.g. the *T* system developed here is, evidently, a part of mathematical logic, but is quite different from the Peano-Russellian system.[1] So is the system of Leśniewski [2] which

---

[1] The relation of *CS* [*KS*] and *NI* [*M*-System] both to each other and to logic is fundamentally solved in: A. Menne, *Logik und Existenz*, Meisenheim 1954.
[2] For a bibliography of his numerous writings cf. *The Journal of Symbolic Logic* 1, 1936,

does not admit the null class. So is the intuitionistic logic [1] and the system of strict implication of Professor Lewis[2], which both differ from the Peano-Russellian logic in other respects.

Thesis 10. The question 'Which of the systems of CS: the traditional or the Peano-Russellian, is true?' is a pseudo-problem

Opinions. On both sides it has been said that the opposite system is false. The earlier mathematical logicians contended that traditional logic contains errors; Thomists argued that mathematical logic (meaning the Boolean or Peano-Russellian system) is false, while the opposite system was said to be the only true one by both parties. There was not only a discussion but a regular quarrel about it.

Proof. Every question about the exclusive truth of one part of a non-exclusive alternative is a pseudo-problem; but the above question is such; Thesis.

The major is evident. The minor is proved by our Theses 8 and 9, as also by the following considerations: The traditional system of CS is our *T* system; the Peano-Russellian system of CS is our *NI* system. Now it has been shown that the *NI* system is a proper part of the *T* system; and we have proved that the *T* system contains no errors, i.e. that it is true. But if the whole is true, the part of it must be also true. Thus both systems are true and there is no real opposition between them, the difference depending on the fact only that one axiom assumed by the *T* system is dropped by the *NI* system.[3]

The whole problem is thus reduced to a matter of practical usefulness. In every science that system should be chosen which is the most convenient for its development.

170, N. 202; also: *Grundzüge eines neuen Systems der Grundlagen der Mathematik* 12, ex: Collectanea Logica 1, 1938; *Einleitende Bemerkungen zur Fortsetzung meiner Mitteilung u.d. Titel 'Grundzüge...'*, ibid.

[1] A good informal account of Intuitionistic Logic may be found in K. Menger, *Der Intuitionismus*, Blätter für Deutsche Philosophie, 4, 1930, 311–325. For formal development cf. Heyting, op. cit. (footnote 3 on page 29).

[2] C. I. Lewis and H. C. Langford, *Symbolic Logic,* New York, 1932.

[3] Thus no relativistic philosophy is involved, for *abstrahentium non est mendacium*, and our *NI* system is just an abstraction from the *T* system. The objection of relativism involved in such considerations has been discussed by us in *La pensée catholique et la logique moderne*, Cracovie 1937, pp. 165f. and pp. 180f.

III

IVO THOMAS

CS(n): AN EXTENSION OF CS*

The formal system which is here presented, and which we designate by the name 'CS(n)' is intended as an extension or remodelling of the system developed by I. M. Bocheński, in his article 'On the Categorical Syllogism'. We shall refer to the original system as 'CS'.[1]

In CS there are deduced the traditional laws of the logical square, of simple and *per accidens* conversion, and twenty-two modes of categorical syllogism, the remaining two, *Barbara* and *Ferio,* being axioms. Other axioms are certain laws of the logic of unanalysed propositions and the axioms, specific to CS, '*Aaa*' and '*Iaa*'. The two syllogistic operators '*A*' and '*I*' are taken as primitive, two others, '*E*' and '*O*', being defined thus:

1. $Eba = NIba$
2. $Oba = NAba$

The basic new feature in CS(n) is the name-negation '*n*', interpreted as the infinitizing negative of traditional logic. Its introduction effects remarkable changes. We are enabled to take only one syllogistic operator, '*A*', as primitive, defining the other three in terms of that one and the two negations, and are further enabled to drop one of the specific axioms, *Barbara,* without any diminution in the laws of the system. We can also deduce the laws of obversion, and those of the contraposition of A and O propositions. The reduction in the number of specific axioms by the omission of *Barbara* is of course the most considerable of these various improvements, and we believe that the formal deduction of twenty-three modes on the basis of '*Aaa*', '*Iaa*' and a single mode is a definitive advance in the theory of categorical syllogism. In the interest of further economy we have defined the operators '*N*', '*C*' and '*K*' in the customary way in terms of '*D*' (disjunction); we shall not, however, make any use of

---

* First published in *Dominican Studies II* (1949) 145–160.
[1] This article owes much to the encouragement and detailed suggestions of the author of CS.

these definitions. Our primitive ideas are thereby reduced to the following:

'*p*', '*q*', '*r*', '*s*',
'*a*', '*b*', '*m*',
'*D*', '*A*',
'*n*'.

There will be seven sections:

1. Additions to the metalogical introduction to CS
2. Change in the rules of deduction of CS
3. Note on the numbering of laws
4. Definitions and axioms
5. Deduction
6. Summary figures, tables and discussion

1. *Additions to the metalogical introduction to CS*

Symbols	*Names*	*Interpretation*
D 1.1 'D' followed by two propositions	exclusion	disjunctive proposition (at the most one of both propositions is true)
D 5.1 '*n*' followed by a name	name-negation	negation of the name following '*n*'
D 7.1 Syllogistic operator followed by two names (*vice* CS D 7).	syllogistic proposition	(as in traditional logic)
D 8.1 Symbols as under 5 and 5.1	name	

D 19.1 '*X* is a term of *Y*' for: '*Y* is a syllogistic proposition and *X* is a name in *Y*'.
(*vice* CS D 19).

D 34 '*X* and *Y* are a contradictory pair' for: '*X* and *Y* are syllogistic propositions and '*CXNY*' and '*CNYX*' are laws of the system'.

D 35 '*X* is the obverse of *Y*' for: '*X* and *Y* are syllogistic propositions and (1) the subjects of *X* and *Y* are of the same shape, (2) the

41

predicate of X is a name of the same shape as that of Y but preceded by 'n', or inversely, (3) if X contains an A-, E-, I- or O-operator, Y contains, respectively, an E-, A-, O-, or I-operator'.

D 36   'X is a converse of Y' for: 'X and Y are syllogistic propositions and (1) the subject of X has the same shape as the predicate of Y, (2) the predicate of X has the same shape as the subject of Y'.

D 36.1 'X is the simple converse of Y' for: 'X is a converse of Y and the syllogistic operators of X and Y are of the same shape'.

D 36.2 'X is the *per accidens* converse of Y' for: 'X is a converse of Y and if one of X and Y contains an A- or E-operator, the other contains, respectively, an I- or O-operator'.

D 36.3 'X is the contrapositive of Y' for: 'X is a converse of Y and names negated in X are not negated in Y and names not negated in X are negated in Y, (4) X and Y contain syllogistic operators of the same shape'.[1]

D 37   'X is subalternate to Y' for 'X and Y are syllogistic propositions and 'CXY' is a law of the system but not 'CYX' '.

D 37.1 'X is a contrary of Y' for: 'X and Y are syllogistic propositions and '$CXNY$' is a law of the system but not '$CNXY$' '.

D 37.2 'X is a subcontrary of Y' for: 'X and Y are syllogistic propositions and '$CNXY$' is a law of the system but not '$CXNY$' '.

2. *Change in the rules of deduction of CS*

The second rule of substitution now reads as follows: *Second rule of substitution:* If X is a law of the system, a substitution of a name for a nominal variable contained in X is a law of the system.

3. *Note on the numbering of laws*

Theorems bearing numbers short of *43* without figures to the right of the decimal point are quotations from CS according to their original numera-

---

[1] D 36.3 enforces the ancient usage. Modern practice would seem not to be standardized. J. N. Keynes (*Studies and Exercises in Formal Logic,* 3rd ed., 1894, pp. 101f.) recognizes his departure from tradition in saying that '*Enab*' is the contrapositive of '*Aba*' and '*Ananb*' its obverted contrapositive. D 35 and D 36.3 reverse this nomenclature, which was also adopted by W. E. Johnson (*Logic,* Pt. I, p. 141, Cambridge, 1921).

tion (with the exception of CS 18 which is our *17*). We use a vacant place in CS, *43*, for the new laws of obversion.

4. Definitions and axioms

1.01	Np	$= Dpp$
1.02	Cpq	$= DpNq$
1.03	Kpq	$= NDpq$
1.04	nna	$= a$
1.05	Eba	$= Abna$
1.06	Iba	$= NAbna$
2.	Oba	$= NAba$
3.	Cpp	
4.	$CCpNqCqNp$	
5.	$CCpqCNqNp$	
6.	$CCpqCCqrCpr$	
7.	$CNNpp$	
8.	$CCKpqrCKNrqNp$	
9.	$CCKpqrCCspCKsqr$	
10.	$CCKpqrCpCqr$	
11.	$CCKpqrCqCpr$	
12.	$CCKpqrCCsqCKpsr$	
13.	$CCKpqrCKpNrNq$	
14.	$CCKpqrCKqpr$	
15.	Aaa	
16.	Iaa	
17.	$CKEmaIbmOba$	
90.01	Hpq	$= KCpqCqp$
90.02	$HpHqHrs$	$= KHpqKHqrKrs$

1.01–*.03* are the customary definitions of negation, implication and conjunction in terms of disjunction. *1.04* embodies the principle of double negation as applied to names. *1.03*–*.06* are our new definitions of '*E*' and '*I*', the latter being undefined in CS. *2* remains the same. *3–17* are taken over unchanged from CS, *Barbara* (CS *17*) being dropped and *Ferio* moving up into its place. *90.01.02* will, together with *90.1* to be deduced later, enable us to assert co-implications, which is more necessary for the display of this system than for that of the original. We have noticed that *3–14* are not independent, but in conformity with the intention of the author of CS we have left them untouched as an otherwise unexceptionable and well-chosen basis on which to proceed at once to the development of the specific system.

5. Deduction

The deduction of the laws of contradiction now proceeds as follows:

$$3 \ p/NAbna \times 1.06 \ I° \times 1.05 \ II° = (i)$$
$$(i) = 22. \ CIbaNEba$$
$$4 \ p/Iba, \ q/Eba = C(i) - 20$$
20.   *CEbaNIba*
$$7 \ p/Abna \times 1.06 \ I° \times 1.05 \ II° = 21$$
21.   *CNIbaEba*
$$3 \ p/NAbna \times 1.05 \ I° \times 1.06 \ II° = 23$$
23.   *CNEbaIba*
$$3 \ p/Oba \times 2 \ II° = 24$$
24.   *CObaNAba*
$$3 \ p/Oba \times 2 \ I° = 25$$
25.   *CNAbaOba*
$$4 \ p/Oba, \ q/Aba = C24 - 26$$
26.   *CAbaNOba*
$$7 \ p/Aba \times 2 = 27$$
27.   *CNObaAba*

$$28.21 - 28.28 = 20 - 27 \ b/nb$$
$$28.31 - 28.38 = 20 - 27 \ a/na$$
$$28.41 - 28.48 = 20 - 27 \ b/nb, \ a/na$$
$$28.51 - 28.58 = 20 - 27 \ b/a, \ a/b$$
$$28.61 - 28.68 = 20 - 27 \ b/na, \ a/b$$
$$28.71 - 28.78 = 20 - 27 \ b/a, \ a/nb$$
$$28.81 - 28.88 = 20 - 27 \ b/na, \ a/nb$$

We have now obtained sixteen contradictory pairs which, after deducing *90.1*, we express in terms of co-implications in the manner of *91.11*.

$$3 \ p/Kpq = (1)$$
$$(1) \ CKpqKpq$$
$$10 \ r/Kpq = C(1) - 90.1$$
90.1   *CpCqKpq*

$90.1\ p/CAbaNOba,\ q/CNObaAba = C26 - C27 - (1)$
$(1)\ KCAbaNObaCNObaAba$
$(1) \times 90.01 = 91.11$

91.11 *HAbaNOba*

Similarly we obtain the following co-implications. Use of *90.1* and *90.01* will in future be tacit.

91.11	*HAbaNOba*	91.21	*HAabNOab*
.12	*HEbaNIba*	.22	*HEabNIab*
.13	*HAnbaNOnba*	.23	*HAnabNOnab*
.14	*HEnbaNINba*	.24	*HEnabNInab*
.15	*HAbnaNObna*	.25	*HAanbNOanb*
.16	*HEbnaNIbna*	.26	*HEanbNIanb*
.17	*HAnbnaNOnbna*	.27	*HAnanbNOnanb*
.18	*HEnbnaNInbna*	.28	*HEnanbNInanb*

Each member of each contradictory pair is next proved to imply and be implied by its obverse.

$3\ p/Eba \times 1.05\ II° = 43.11$

43.11 *CEbaAbna*

$3\ p/Eba \times 1.05\ I° = 43.12$

43.12 *CAbnaEba*

$43.11\ a/na \times 1.04 = 43.13$

43.13 *CEbnaAba*

$43.12\ a/na \times 1.04 = 43.14$

43.14 *CAbaEbna*

$24\ a/na \times 1.06 = 43.15$

43.15 *CObnaIba*

$25\ a/na \times 1.06 = 43.16$

43.16 *CIbaObna*

$43.15\ a/na \times 1.04 = 43.17$

43.17 *CObaIbna*

$43.16\ a/na \times 1.04 = 43.18$

43.18 *CIbnaOba*

$43.21 - 43.28 = 43.11 - 43.18\ b/nb$
$43.31 - 43.38 = 43.11 - 43.18\ b/a,\ a/b$
$43.41 - 43.48 = 43.11 - 43.18\ b/na,\ a/b$

45

There follows a table of the co-implications just proved (*92*).

92.11	*HAbaEbna*	*92.21*	*HEnabAnanb*
.12	*HAbnaEba*	*.22*	*HEabAanb*
.13	*HObnaIba*	*.23*	*HIabOanb*
.14	*HObaIbna*	*.24*	*HInabOnanb*
.15	*HAabEanb*	*.25*	*HEnbaAnbna*
.16	*HAnabEnanb*	*.26*	*HEnbnaAnba*
.17	*HOnabInanb*	*.27*	*HInbnaOnba*
.18	*HOabIanb*	*.28*	*HInbaOnbna*

For the contrasting of CS(n) with CS it is important to make it clear that the *Barbara* mode which we have dropped from the original axioms is not used in proving the laws of conversion and of the logical square. We therefore quote the proof of *Datisi,* and demonstrate those laws. In the next proof we use the number which *Ferio* has in our axioms, *viz. 17.*

$$8 \; p/Eba, \; q/Imb, \; r/Oma = C17b/m, \; m/b - (1)$$
$$(1) \quad CKNOmaImbNEba$$
$$9 \; p/NOma, \; q/Imb, \; r/NEba, \; s/Ama = C(1) - C26b/m - (2)$$
$$(2) \quad CKAmaImbNEba$$
$$6 \; p/KAmaImb, \; q/NEba, \; r/Iba = C(2) - C23 - 30$$
$$30. \quad CKAmaImbIba \qquad \text{(Datisi)}$$
$$10 \; p/Abb, \; q/Iba, \; r/Iab = C30a/b, \; b/a, \; m/b - C15a/b - 31$$
$$31. \quad CIbaIab$$
$$31 \; b/a, \; a/b = 31.1$$
$$31.1 \; CIabIba$$
$$11 \; p/Aba, \; q/Ibb, \; r/Iba = C30m/b - C16a/b - 32$$
$$32. \quad CAbaIba$$
$$6 \; p/Aba, \; q/Iba, \; r/Iab = C32 - C31 - 33$$
$$33. \quad CAbaIab$$
$$5 \; p/Iab, \; q/Iba = C31.1 - (1)$$
$$(1) \quad CNIbaNIab$$
$$6 \; p/Eba, \; q/NIba, \; r/NIab = C20 - C(1) - (2)$$
$$(2) \quad CEbaNIab$$
$$6 \; p/Eba, \; q/NIab, \; r/Eab = C(2) - C21b/a, \; a/b - 34$$
$$34. \quad CEbaEab$$
$$34 \; b/a, \; a/b = 34.1$$

34.1 CEabEba

        5 p/Aba, q/Iba × 2 = C32 − (1)

      (1)   *CNIbaOba*

        6 p/Eba, q/NIba, r/Oba = C20 − C(1) − 35

35.   *CEbaOba*

        6 p/Eba, q/Eab, r/Oab = C34 − C35b/a, a/b − 36

36.   *CEbaOab*

        5 p/Aba, q/Iba = C32 − 37

37.   *CNIbaNAba*

        5 p/Eba, q/Oba = C35 − 38

38.   *CNObaNEba*

        6 p/Aba, q/NOba, r/NEba = C26 − C38 − 39

39.   *CAbaNEba*

        35 × 2 = 40

40.   *CEbaNAba*

        37 × 2 = 41

41.   *CNIbaOba*

        6 p/NOba, q/NEba, r/Iba = C38 − C23 − 42

42.   *CNObaIba*

The laws of contraposition for *A* and *O* propositions can readily be deduced individually from *31* and *34* by the mere applications of definitions. But they may be gained wholesale, since by *31, 31.1, 34, 34.1* all *E* and *I* propositions are proved co-implicant with their simple converses. The various pairs will be found on the inside places of the corresponding lines in the columns of *92*. We are thus enabled to state the following series of co-implications (*93*).

93.1   *HAbaHEbnaHEnabAnanb*

  .2   *HAbnaHEbaHEabAanb*

  .3   *HObnaHIbaHIabOanb*

  .4   *HObaHIbnaHInabOnanb*

  .5   *HAabHEanbHEnbaAnbna*

  .6   *HAnabHEnanbHEnbnaAnba*

  .7   *HOnabHInanbHInbnaOnba*

  .8   *HOabHIanbHInbaOnbna*

Lines *1* and *4, 2* and *3, 5* and *8, 6* and *7* are, respectively, contradictories.

The first and last propositions in each line, all either *A* or *O* propositions, show the laws of contraposition (*94*).

94.1   *HAbaAnanb*
  .2   *HAbnaAanb*
  .3   *HObnaOanb*
  .4   *HObaOnanb*
  .5   *HAabAnbna*
  .6   *HAnabAnba*
  .7   *HOnabOnba*
  .8   *HOabOnbna*

The laws of contrariety:

39.   *CAbaNEba*
40.   *CEbaNAba*

show that, in *93*, the following lines are contrary:

line *1* (containing '*Aba*' and '*Ananb*') to lines *2* ('*Eba*') and *6* ('*Enanb*')
line *5* (containing '*Aab*' and '*Anbna*') to lines *2* ('*Eab*') and *6* ('*Enbna*')

Similarly the laws of subcontrariety:

41.   *CNIbaOba*
42.   *CNObaIba*

show that
line *3* (containing '*Iba*' and '*Iab*') is subcontrary to lines *4* ('*Oba*') and *8* ('*Oab*')
line *7* ('*Inanb*' and '*Inbna*') to lines *4* ('*Onanb*') and *8* ('*Onbna*').

And again, the laws of subalternation:

32.   *CAbaIba*
37.   *CNIbaNAba*

show the subalternation of lines *3* and *7* to each of *1* and *5*, of lines *4* and *8* to each of *2* and *6*.

At this point the proofs of *Cesare*, *Celarent* and *Barbara* might follow, and we should then have in our system all the laws from which the remainder of the modes are proved in CS. Once *Barbara* was obtained, the methods of proof might remain unchanged. But since some new methods are available, and we shall later display the intra-systematic grouping of modes on another basis than that of syllogistic figure, we shall adopt in some cases another course of deduction, and here cease to correlate the numeration of our laws with that of CS.

Ferio (17) and *Datisi* (30) are already in the system. We proceed to the remaining four modes of what we shall call 'Group I'.

$$17\ a/na \times 2\ a/na = (1)$$
(1) *CKEmnaIbmNAbna*
$$9\ p/Emna, q/Ibm, r/NAbna, s/Ama \times 1.06 =$$
$$= C(1) - C43.14\ b/m - 50$$
50. *CKAmaIbmIba*   (Darii)
$$13\ p/Ama, q/Ibm, r/Iba = C50 - (1)$$
(1) *CKAmaNIbaNIbm*
$$6\ p/KAamNIbm, q/NIba, r/Eba = C(1)m/a, a/m - C21 - (2)$$
(2) *CKAamNIbmEba*
$$12\ p/Aam, q/NIbm, r/Eba, s/Ebm = C(2) - C21 - 51$$
51. *CKAamEbmEba*   (Camestres)
$$51\ m/nm \times 1.06b/a, a/m = (1)$$
(1) *CKEamEbnmEba*
$$12\ p/Eam, q/Ebnm, r/Eba, s/Abm = C(1) - C43.13a/m - 52$$
52. *CKEamAbmEba*   (Cesare)
$$30\ a/na \times 1.05b/m = (1)$$
(1) *CKEmaImbIbna*
$$6\ p/KEmaImb, q/Ibna, r/Oba = C(1) - C43.18 - 53$$
53. *CKEmaImbOba*   (Ferison)

We now pass to the six modes which we shall call 'Group III', Group II being more conveniently deduced later.

$$9\ p/Eam, q/Abm, r/Eba, s/Ema = C52 - C34b/m - 54$$
54. *CKEmaAbmEba*   (Celarent)
$$9\ p/Emna, q/Abm, r/Ebna, s/Ama =$$
$$= C54a/na - C43.14b/m - (1)$$
(1) *CKAmaAbmEbna*
$$6\ p/KAmaAbm, q/Ebna, r/Aba = C(1) - C43.13 - 55$$
55. *CKAmaAbmAba*   (Barbara)
    55 was axiom *17* in CS.
$$13\ p/Aam, q/Aba, r/Abm \times 2a/m \times 2 = C55m/a, a/m - 56$$
56. *CKAamObmOba*   (Baroco)
$$8\ p/Aba, q/Amb, r/Ama \times 2b/m \times 2 = C55m/b, b/m - 57$$

57. *CKOmaAmbOba*   (Bocardo)
     9 p/Ema, q/Ibm, r/Oba, s/Eam = C17 — C34.1b/m — 58
58. *CKEamIbmOba*   (Festino)
     9 p/Omna, q/Amb, r/Obna, s/Ima = C57a/na — C43.16b/m — (1)
   (1)   *CKImaAmbObna*
     6 p/KImaAmb, q/Obna, r/Iba = C(1) — C43.15 — 59
59. *CKImaAmbIba*   (Disamis)

There follow the three modes which we shall call 'Group II'.

     9 p/Ima, q/Amb, r/Iba, s/Iam = C59 — C31.1b/m — 60
60. *CKIamAmbIba*   (Dimaris)
     9 p/Ema, q/Imb, r/Oba, s/Eam = C53 — C34.1b/m — 61
61. *CKEamImbOba*   (Fresison)
     12 p/Aam, q/Ebm, r/Eba, s/Emb = C51 — C34.1a/m — 62
62. *CKAamEmbEba*   (Camenes)

There follow the six modes which we shall call 'Group IV'.

     6 p/KAmaAbm, q/Aba, r/Iba — C55 — C32 — 63
63. *CKAmaAbmIba*   (Barbari)
     6 p/KAamEbm, q/Eba, r/Oba = C51 — C35 — 64
64. *CKAamEbmOba*   (Camestrop)
     12 p/Ema, q/Imb, r/Oba, s/Amb = C53 — C32 — 65
65. *CKEmaAmbOba*   (Felapton)
     6 p/KEmaAbm, q/Eba, r/Oba = C54 — C35 — 66
66. *CKEmaAbmOba*   (Celaront)
     6 p/KEamAbm, q/Eba, r/Oba = C52 — C35 — 67
67. *CKEamAbmOba*   (Cesaro)
     12 p/Ama, q/Imb, r/Iba, s/Amb = C30 — C32 — 68
68. *CKAmaAmbIba*   (Darapti)

There remain the three modes which we shall call 'Group V'.

     9 p/Iam, q/Amb, r/Iba, s/Aam = C60 — C32 — 69
69. *CKAamAmbIba*   (Bamalip)
     6 p/KAamEmb, q/Eba, r/Oba = C62 — C35 — 70
70. *CKAamEmbOba*   (Camenop)
     12 p/Eam, q/Imb, r/Oba, s/Amb = C61 — C32b/m, a/b — 71
71. *CKEamAmbOba*   (Fesapo)

6. Summary figures, tables and discussion

(a)

The relations found to hold both intra- and inter-linearly in *93* can be displayed in the accompanying Figure I.

FIGURE I

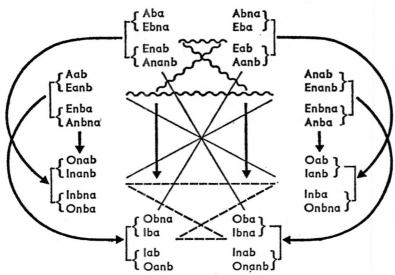

——————— marks contradictions, the first laws obtained.
{   marks obversions, the second series obtained.
[marks simple conversions and consequent contrapositions.
——————→ marks subalternations.
⁓⁓⁓⁓⁓⁓ marks contrariety.
- - - - - - marks subcontrariety.

The thirty-two propositions appearing in the figure exhaust the combinations of each syllogistic operator with one from each of the pairs *a-na*, *b-nb*, so the system is in that sense complete. No dependence can be proved to hold between, respectively, '*Aba*', and '*Anbna*' '*Eba*' and '*Enbna*', '*Iba*' and '*Inbna*', '*Oba*' and '*Onbna*' or the respective co-implicants of each.

These relations of independence are shown in Figure II which may be superimposed on Figure I.

51

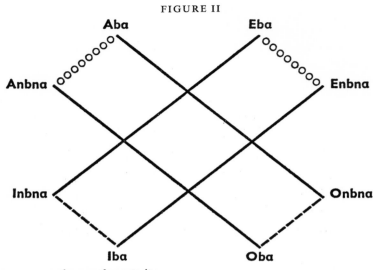

FIGURE II

o o o o o marks complementarity.
- - - - - - marks subcomplementarity.
———————— marks contra-complementarity.[1]

The following table will be found useful for descriptive purposes. We use the name 'inverse' for the *per accidens* converse (or, as we call it in the table, 'Converse (2)') with both terms negated.

TABLE I

Basic form	*Aba*	*Oba*	*Iba*	*Eba*	Basic form
Obverse	*Ebna*	*Ibna*	*Obna*	*Abna*	Obverse
Converse obverse	*Enab*	*Inab*	*Oanb*	*Aanb*	Obverse converse
Contrapositive	*Ananb*	*Onanb*	*Iab*	*Eab*	Converse
Obverse conv. (2)	*Oanb*			*Oab*	Converse (2)
Converse (2)	*Iab*			*Ianb*	Obv. conv. (2)
Converse conv. (2)	*Iba*			*Inba*	Conv. obv. conv. (2)
Obv. conv. conv. (2)	*Obna*			*Onbna*	Contrap. conv. (2)
Obverse inverse	*Onab*			*Onanb*	Inverse
Inverse	*Inanb*			*Inab*	Obv. inverse
Converse inverse	*Inbna*			*Ibna*	Conv. obv. inverse
Obv. conv. inverse	*Onba*			*Oba*	Contrap. inverse

[1] This nomenclature was devised by W. E. Johnson; cf. J. N. Keynes, loc. cit., p. 100, n.1.

(b)

With regard to our single syllogistic axiom, the possible alternatives which will yield all the laws of CS(n) may best be shown from the tables which follow.

TABLE II

SYSTEMATIC RELATIONS OF MODES IN CS(n)

1	2	3	4
{ Darii	Camestres	Ferison	{ I = = = II *Dimaris Camenes Fresison*
{ Ferio	Cesare	Datisi	
{ Celarent	Festino	Disamis	{ III
{ Barbara	Baroco	Bocardo	
{ Celaront	Cesaro	Darapti	{ IV = = = V *Bamalip Camenop Fesapo*
{ Barbari	Camestrop	Felapton	

Arabic numerals mark figures of syllogism, roman ones systematic groups.

Within each line of three modes passage can be made by the principle of transposition.

Within parentheses passage can be made from one line to another, in the first and third figures by obverting the major premiss and conclusion, in the second figure by obverting both premisses. The consequent negation of major or middle terms may be removed by further negating them. The laws of obversion do not depend on those of conversion or the square.

= = = = marks passage from one group to another that can only be made by simple conversion.

―――――→ marks passage from one group to another that can only be made by means of some law of subalternation.

- - - - - -→ marks passage between one group and another that can only be made directly by means of *per accidens* conversion. We omit to signify this relation as holding between Groups I and V, II and IV.

Clearly the whole set of modes can only be obtained if some one from Groups I, II or III is taken as primitive. It must therefore be investigated which modes from those groups, in conjunction with '*Aaa*' and '*Iaa*', yield any laws of simple conversion. For the sake of completeness we give in Table II an analysis of what laws of conversion and subalternation are yielded by what modes in proofs analogous to those of our laws *31* and *32*. If an *E* conversion or *A — I* subalternation is given, the corresponding *I* conversion or *E — O* subalternation is of course obtainable without the assistance of any other mode.

It is evident from the table that a primitive mode from either of Groups IV and V will yield only the rest of its group. One from Group III will

53

TABLE III

Group	Mode	Simple Conversion	*Per Accidens* Conversion	Direct Sub-alternation
I	*Darii*			*A—I*
	Cesare	*E*		
	Ferison			*E—O*
	Ferio			*E—O*
	Datisi	*I*		*A—I*
II	*Dimaris*	*I*	*A*	
	Camenes	*E*		
	Fresison		*E*	
III	*Festino*		*E*	
	Disamis		*A*	
IV V	Every mode in these groups yields just one law of *per accidens* conversion or direct subalternation.			

yield the remainder of the Group and Group V (Group IV being directly subaltern to Group III, and so not obtainable). Either of Groups I and II have all the requirements for obtaining the full system. It is interesting that *Datisi* and *Dimaris* alone give both simple conversion and one form of subalternation, with the other resulting as an immediate consequence, and they may therefore be judged to be on an equality of systematic pre-eminence.

(On March 16th, just four weeks after this article had gone to press, we heard from J. M. Bocheński of the newly received *Elements of Formal Logic* by A. Weigner (Poznań, 1948) containing a full treatment of categorical syllogism on very similar lines to ours. The two works are wholly independent, but priority must be accorded to the Polish author.)

IV

ALBERT MENNE

SOME RESULTS OF INVESTIGATION
OF THE SYLLOGISM
AND THEIR PHILOSOPHICAL CONSEQUENCES

Investigation of the classical system of the categorical syllogism has produced in the last ten years very fruitful results, thanks to the introduction of the highly polished tools offered by the modern logical calculus. Since definitive answers to most of the important questions have been obtained, research at this point even appears to have been concluded. Therefore, in the following, the most important results will be sketched and their ontological consequences illuminated.

I. AXIOMATIC

As I. Thomas has shown in the previous work, the dyadic A-operator and a monadic operator of term negation, which can be interpreted in class calculus as the complement, losing thereby its special character, suffice as primitive symbols for the construction of the system of categorical syllogism. Because the three remaining syllogistic operators E, I and O that can be defined from A with the help of the complement and negation, and conversely, because A is definable from them in the same manner, one of the three other syllogistic operators could be employed in place of A.

One could also work without the complement, as Bocheński has done in Chapter II of this work, and take both syllogistic operators A and I as primitive. (However, one cannot take two arbitrary dyadic operators, but must in addition use at most A and E, E and O or I and O). By such a procedure, however, one cannot represent (much less prove) the laws of obversion, contraposition and inversion and must assume two syllogisms as axioms, while by employment of the complement only one axiom of this sort has to be used. Therefore, it seems to me useful to construct the axiom system on the basis of the two primitive symbols of the first kind. One thereby ends up with three axioms, three definitions and two rules (which have analogues in the propositional calculus). From the logic of propositions are added negation N, conjunction K and implication C, as well as the definitions possible through these, i.e., disjunction D, alternation V (which may be characterized here in a way such as to avoid confusion with the syllogistic operator A), equivalence H (which is characterized here in a manner such as to avoid confusion with the syllogistic operator E) and exclusive alternation J. In addition, there are eight rules.[1]

Axioms:

   1. ⊢ $HAabAb'a'$
   2. ⊢ $CAabNAab'$
   3. ⊢ $CKAmbAamAab$

Definitions:

   4. Eab = df Aab'
   5. Iab = df $NAab'$
   6. Oab = df $NAab$

Special Rules:

   7. For a term variable (a, b, m and their complements) another term variable may be substituted if at the same time all those terms isomorphic with the term variables (a, b, m and their complements) are replaced by terms isomorphic with the substituted term.
   8. A double complement cancels itself (thus, for example, a'' is equal to a).

Definitions from the propositional calculus:

   9. Dpq = df $CpNq$
  10. Vpq = df $CNpq$
  11. Hpq = df $KCpqCqp$
  12. Jpq = df $NHpq$

Rules from the propositional calculus:

  13. A propositional variable may be replaced by a syllogistic proposition provided that all propositional variables isomorphic with that proposi-

---

[1] The system presented here represents a slight modification to that realized for the first time in A. Menne, *Logik und Existenz*, Meisenheim, 1954, p. 57. For the saving of a rule, I am indebted to an allusion of Prof. Joseph Dopp. Of course all propositional functors could be defined by means of D and rules deduced from the one axiom of *Nicod*, but in that case, the entire propositional calculus must be presupposed while in this case we wish to show only that one can make do with a frugal part of that. The assertion symbol '⊢' marks laws of the system.

tional variable are replaced by propositions isomorphic with the syllog-
tic proposition.

14. A sentence may be replaced by a suitably chosen sentence equivalent
to it.

15. *Kpq* is equivalent to *Kqp*.

16. *NNp* is equivalent to *p*.

17. If ⊢ *Hpq*, then ⊢ *Hqp*.

18. If ⊢ *CKpqr*, then ⊢ *CKpNrNq*.

19. If ⊢ *CKpqr* and ⊢ *Csq*, then ⊢ *CKpsr*.

20. If ⊢ *Cpq* and ⊢ *Cqr*, then ⊢ *Cpr*.

All the classical laws of equipollence, conversion, contraposition, logical
square as well as the twenty-four syllogisms (including the four 'contro-
versial' and the five weakened syllogisms) can be easily enough derived in
this system. The derivation itself may be omitted here.[1] To make up for
that, the originality of the system which results from 1–20 shall be somewhat illuminated.

An expedient from the propositional calculus makes it possible to
employ the implication *C* in place of in the usual sense also in the sense
of 'strong implication'.[2] No use is made of the 'paradoxes' of implication
and De Morgan's laws.

Axiom 1 assumes contraposition of the *A*-operator This is a weaker
structural property than reflexivity which is assumed by most other
axiom systems; for to be sure, contraposition can be gotten from
reflexivity with the help of transitivity, but not conversely. Contraposition
is not a specific property of the *A*-operator; it also belongs, for example, to
implication, equivalence, exclusive alternation, the functors of equality
or inclusion of classes and relations.

Axiom 2, on the contrary, appears to hold specifically of the *A*-operator.
It is the basis of the subalternation rule and impure conversion and
contraposition, the contested and weakened syllogisms, dependent on
that rule. If one drops the *A*-operator, then all these rules also fail. The
A-operator can then be immediately interpreted as inclusion within the class
calculus or as formal implication within the predicate calculus. It follows

---

[1] It is to be found in Menne; loc. cit. pp. 57f.
[2] See A. Menne, *Implikation und Syllogistik*, Zeitschrift für philosophische Forschung XI (1957), 375–386; W Ackermann, *Begründung einer strengen Implikation*,
Journal of Symbolic Logic 21 (1956), 113–128.

further from Axiom 2 that the complement is a stronger denial than negation, for ⊦ $CAab'NAab$ is indeed valid but not the converse, $CNAabAab'$.

Axiom 3 presumes transitivity for the A-operator. That is true in most axiom systems. This property holds not only for the A-operator since, for example, implication, conjunction, equivalence, class inclusion and inclusion with regard to relations are transitive.

Rules 7 and 8 correspond to Rules 13 and 16 in the propositional calculus and have analogues in the class calculus and the relation calculus.

I have proved the consistency and independence of the three axioms in *Logik und Existenz*, page 62.

II. INTERPRETATION

We define:

21. $\alpha \varsigma \beta = $ df $K \alpha \varsigma \beta K \exists! \alpha \exists! \beta$ (definite subsumption).
22. $\alpha \ne \beta = $ df $E! \alpha \cap \beta$ (definite community).

If now the class variables 'α', 'β', 'γ' are associated with the term variables 'a', 'b', 'm', class complement '—' with the complement '/' and definite subsumption 'ς' with the A-operator, then axioms 1–3 and definitions 4–6 are forthcoming as laws of the class calculus.

23. ⊦ $H(\alpha \varsigma \beta)(- \beta \varsigma - \alpha)$
24. ⊦ $C(\alpha \varsigma \beta) N (\alpha \varsigma - \beta)$
25. ⊦ $CK(\gamma \varsigma \beta)(\alpha \varsigma \gamma)(\alpha \varsigma \beta)$
26. ⊦ $H(\alpha \varsigma - \beta)(\alpha \varsigma - \beta)$
27. ⊦ $H(\alpha \ne \beta) N (\alpha \varsigma - \beta)$
28. ⊦ $H(\alpha \ne - \beta) N (\alpha \varsigma \beta)$

Rule 7 remains valid as a rule of substitution in the class calculus. Rule 8 corresponds to the law

29. ⊦ $- - \alpha = \alpha$.

It should be noted that in definitions 21 and 22 only non-empty classes and class intersections are permitted. Definite subsumption and community therefore represent special functions which are possible only for classes that are distinct from the null class; so that complementation remains possible, they must also be distinct from the universal class.

The classical system of the categorical syllogism can consequently be interpreted as a special case of the class calculus, or more precisely, of the definite class calculus (that is, the class calculus without the null and universal classes).

The interpretation of the syllogistic operator *A* by means of formal implication so often attempted hitherto, besides the well-known lack of subalternation and the laws dependent upon that, has as a consequence that indefinite classes (null and universal classes) can replace the terms *a, b, m*; this yields, in addition to the seven relations, cited in III, eight further class relations.

III. DEFINITE CLASS RELATIONS

Two definite classes (distinct from the null and universal classes) can occur in exactly seven different relations.[1]

30. $\alpha \doteqdot \beta$ definite equality
31. $\alpha \subsetneq \beta$ definite inclusion
32. $\alpha \mathbin{?} \beta$ definite enclosure
33. $\alpha \mathbin{\between} \beta$ intersection
34. $- \alpha \mathbin{?} \beta$
35. $\alpha \subsetneq - \beta$
36. $\alpha \doteqdot - \beta$

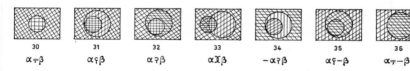

30	31	32	33	34	35	36
$\alpha \doteqdot \beta$	$\alpha \subsetneq \beta$	$\alpha \mathbin{?} \beta$	$\alpha \mathbin{\between} \beta$	$-\alpha \mathbin{?} \beta$	$\alpha \subsetneq -\beta$	$\alpha \doteqdot -\beta$

Likewise, it can now be shown [2] that to the four classical propositional forms *A, E, I* and *O* correspond alternations of the seven definite class relations; indeed, the following are valid:

36. $\vdash HAabV (\alpha \doteqdot \beta)(\alpha \subsetneq \beta)$
37. $\vdash HEabV (\alpha \doteqdot - \beta)(\alpha \subsetneq - \beta)$
38. $\vdash HIabV (\alpha \doteqdot \beta) V (\alpha \subsetneq \beta) V (\alpha \mathbin{?} \beta) V (\alpha \mathbin{\between} \beta)(- \alpha \subsetneq \beta)$
39. $\vdash HOabV (\alpha \mathbin{?} \beta) V (\alpha \mathbin{\between} \beta) V (- \alpha \subsetneq \beta) V (\alpha \subsetneq - \beta)(\alpha \doteqdot - \beta)$

Likewise, all classical laws of syllogistic can be deduced within the class

---

[1] A more detailed proof of this is to be found in Menne, *Logik und Existenz*, pp. 48 f. Compare further A. Menne, *Zur Wahrheitswertstruktur des Urteils*, Methodos I (1950), 52f. Concerning the history of class relations, see *Logik und Existenz*, pp. 45f.
[2] Menne, loc. cit., 52f.

calculus as a result of this interpretation. Moreover, it can be demonstrated when relations of syllogistic propositions that are not universally valid are satisfiable. Thus, for example, the pure conversion of *Aab* is valid if the first term of the alternation, that is, the definite equality, corresponds in the individual case to the *A*-proposition. Through knowledge of the class relations that sometimes are the basis of the propositions, numerous other syllogisms [1] and conversion laws [2] can be constructed. If one makes use of the seven definite class relations in place of the four classical propositions, the conclusions become uncommonly fruitful; the forty-nine possible syllogisms of each figure would yield a conclusion in forty-eight cases, in thirty-two of which even a strictly univocal class relation – to be precise, a definite class relation – appears in the conclusion while in sixteen cases, alternations of definite class relations appear. Only the forty-ninth case ($K[\alpha \between \gamma][\gamma \between \beta]$) furnishes no information since the alternation of all seven definite class relations follows as conclusion. Among the sixteen cases there appears twice a three-part alternation which may be of special interest; it follows, for example, from 33 and 32 as premisses [3]:

$$\vdash CK(\gamma \between \beta)(\alpha \,?\, \gamma) \, VV(\alpha \,?\, \beta)(\alpha \between \beta)(-\alpha \,\varsigma\, \beta)$$

If we designate this three-part alternation as a *U*-proposition, then it follows, that:

40. $\vdash HUabKIabOab$.

The *U*-proposition can thus be obtained as a conjunction from the *I*- and *O*-proposition. Further:

41. $\vdash HUabKIabNAab$.

It is therefore a particular affirmative proposition from which the possibility that it can also be a universal affirmative proposition is positively excluded. While the *I*-proposition can be interpreted, 'at least some', the *U*-proposition is to be interpreted 'only some'. Let it be called for this reason 'strict particular' proposition. It is to be noted here that since the 'strict-particular' proposition together with the *A*- and *E*-proposition form a three-valued system [4], for the following is valid:

---

[1] For examples see Menne, loc. cit., pp. 94 f.
[2] See Menne, loc. cit., pp. 76f.
[3] Menne, loc. cit., p. 87.
[4] About three-valued logic see Bocheński-Menne, *Grundriss der Logistik*, 2nd ed. Paderborn 1962, pp. 100f. and the literature stated there.

42. ⊢ $HUabUab'$
43. ⊢ $HAabEab'$
44. ⊢ $HEabAab'$
45. ⊢ $DAabUab$
46. ⊢ $DEabUab$
47. ⊢ $DAabEab$

If the value 1 be assigned to A, the value 0 to E, 1/2 to U and the complement assigned to negation, then it appears that U – as in the three-valued calculus – in conformity with 42, is invariant with respect to negation while in conformity with 43 and 44, A becomes E and conversely. 45 to 47 show that those three propositional forms constitute a trichotomy, that is, mutually exclude each other. A glance at the class relations which contain their alternation shows that together they exhaust all seven possibilities.

IV. INVERSION

The simultaneous employment of conversion and contraposition to a proposition, results in inversion which leads to new forms of proposition The designation '··' introduced by me [1] for that purpose seems to have met with approval. [2] Inverse propositions are found for the first time in De Morgan. [3] H. Gericke also obtains the four inverses in his work *Algebraische Betrachtungen zu den Aristotelischen Syllogismen* (Arch. der Math. III (1952); 421–433). Inversion is universally valid only in impure form.

48. ⊢ $CAabĬab$
49. ⊢ $CEabÖab$
50. ⊢ $CÄabIab$
51. ⊢ $CËabOab$

Inverse propositions, nevertheless, are suited for simplifying and fundamentally rounding out the representation of classical systems and consequently making possible the representation of numerous conclusions which

---

[1] *Logik und Existenz*, p. 70.
[2] See, for example, Jürgen von Kempski, *Charles S. Peirce und der Pragmatismus*, Stuttgart 1952, pp. 103f., Paul Lorenzen, *Über die Syllogismen als Relationenmultiplikationen*, Archiv für mathematische Logik und Grundlagenforschung 3 (1957), 113, in the Modus-Names.
[3] Augustus de Morgan, *Formal Logic*, London 1847, pp. 61f.

are frequently considered impossible of representation, especially on the basis of the so-called *Peiorems (Conclusio sequiter partem peiorem)*. In any case, conclusions can also be obtained from two universal negative premisses, and what is more, it is always possible to obtain a conclusion from two universal premisses as can be deduced from our axioms. The following are offered as examples:

52. $\vdash CKAmbAamÖab$ (Garderönt)
53. $\vdash CKEmbEamĬab$ (Helenï) [1]
54. $\vdash CKImbEamÖab$ (Liberö)
55. $\vdash CKOmbEamĬab$ (Noverï)

Conclusions 53 and 54 are valid because of the convertibility of the premisses in all four figures. As an example, let 55 be proved here, which contradicts the scholastic rule, *ex mere negativis nil sequitur* as well as 53. For this we assume only the definition of the inverse particular affirmative judgments:

56. $Ĭab = $ df $Ia'b'$
   $3 \times 18 \times 15, I \times 1, II \times 1, III \times 1 \times (5a'/m', b/a) = 57$
57. $CKNAb'a'AmbIm'a$
   57. $b/m' \times 8, a/b' \times 8, m/a, I \times (6a/m), II \times (4b/m), III \times 56 = $
   $= 55$ q. e. d.

V. PHILOSOPHICAL CONSEQUENCES

The classical syllogistic can be applied to our abstract thought and the states of reality it reflects only if the structures defined by axioms 1–3 can be related to the corresponding structures in our thought and these to the corresponding structures of the states of reality. History affords the experience that logic has been successfully applied to scientific thought and this in turn to reality. Thus, axioms 1–3 also represent certain ontological structures of real beings. 1 and 3, which reappear in very many relations, seem to be universal structures, while 2 is more specialized and restricted to the existence of individuals. As a result of 2, the classical syllogism is restricted to non-empty worlds, as 21 and 22 prove.

30 and 36, resulting from definite class relations, are possible only in a world with at least two distinct individuals; 31, 32, 34 and 35 presume at

---

[1] A proof of *Helenï* can be found in A. Menne, *Beweis und Negation,* Act. XI Congr. Int. Phil., Bruxelles, 1953, Vol. V, 94.

least three distinct individuals; 33 even presumes four distinct individuals.[1] According to with 36–39, the four classical propositions are alternations of two, respectively five, distinct definite class relations. The classical syllogism rests therefore upon the ontological presupposition that at least three, respectively four, distinct individuals exist.

All laws of the categorical syllogistic remain valid when all syllogistic operators appearing are replaced by their inverses. Syllogistic can consequently be constructed in two isomorphic systems. Nevertheless, we are concerned with two distinct systems, for a single proposition is in no way equivalent to its inverse. Both propositional forms can appear together in laws, as 48–55 demonstrate. H. Gericke, in the work already mentioned, has succeeded in establishing besides the classical, four additional propositional forms which correspond to our inverses. P. Lorenzen [2] likewise has hit upon these four additional propositional forms as a result of treatment of the syllogism as the multiplication relation. J. v. Kempski [2] employs at least the two inverses, $\ddot{A}$ and $\ddot{O}$ for rounding out the syllogistic. Keynes uses all four.[3] The founding of strong implication within the frame of syllogistic likewise requires them.[4] All this shows that inversion is no mere trifle, but that it corresponds to an ontological structure of being; particularly, the employment of equivalence, exclusive alternation and equality, among others, leaves it invariant. Nevertheless, it appears idle to speculate whether the dual character of finite ontological structures attested by the inverses manifests itself in reality (perhaps in microphysics). The strict-particular proposition shows conclusively that three-valued calculi can also be logically relevant and that certain ontological structures correspond to them, for 42–47 are applicable to every set having at least two members: in a class, all students may be blond; it is possible that no student is blond, and there may be only one blond student if there is at the same time only one student who is not blond.

---

[1] An establishment of this conclusion can be found in *Logik und Existenz*, pp. 123f.
[2] See footnote 2 on page 61.
[3] J. N. Keynes, *Studies and Exercises in Formal Logic*, 4th edition, London 1906, p. 141.
[4] See the work cited first in footnote 2 on page 57.

V

I. M. BOCHENSKI

FORMALIZATION OF A SCHOLASTIC SOLUTION
OF THE PARADOX OF THE 'LIAR'

Paulus Venetus [1] (died 1429) enumerates no fewer than fourteen distinct solutions of the paradox of the 'Liar' [2] of which one corresponds precisely to the modern; the author nevertheless declines all of them and offers another, the fifteenth. This solution comes about from the distinction of two modes of meaning: (a) the meaning (*significatio*) with no further determination, (b) the 'precise and adequate' meaning (*significatio vraecisa et adaequata*). A proposition means in the first place precisely what it means and nothing else; in the second place, it means *also* that it is itself true.

Moreover, what one may also observe from this distinction is that in any case the paradox of the 'Liar' appears only in interpretation (a) but not in (b). We will show this by formalization of the two proofs.

We take as the basis of our exposition the two-valued propositional logic of Łukasiewicz. As is well known, the functors in this system are always written *in front* of their arguments. '*N*', '*A*', '*C*', '*K*' correspond at any given time to '∼', 'V', '⊃', '.' in the Peano-Russellian notation. To this system, we add the following symbols:

---

[1] *Logica Magna,* Venetis 1499 (Hain 12.505) and *Summulae Logicales* (without title and page divisions, Bibl. Nat. Paris Res. 69).

[2] The paradox of the 'Liar' possesses numerous distinct forms. The simplest is the following formulation of the question: Is the isolated proposition 'I lie' made without any association, true or false? If we assume that the proposition is *true,* then it is accordingly agreed that I lie, i.e., that I say an *untruth;* therefore, the proposition is *false.* But if now we assume that the proposition is false, then I have asserted, to be sure, that already through the confirmation, I lie, that is, I have asserted something correct and so the proposition is *true.* From the assumption of truth follows falsity. Since the turn of the century, numerous other paradoxes have been known, and also methods for their avoidance. See Bocheński-Menne, *Grundriß der Logistik* 2nd ed., Paderborn, 1962, § 17. Concerning the history of the 'Liar' in antiquity, see A. Rüstow, *Der Lügner* (Diss. Erlangen), 1910 and I. M. Bocheński, *Ancient Formal Logic,* Amsterdam 1951, pp. 101f. – For the Middle Ages: J. Salamucha: *Pojawienie się zagadnień antynominalnych na gruncie logiki średniowiecznej.* Przegląd Filozoficzny 40 (1937) 320–343, and E. A. Moody, *Truth and Consequences in Medieval Logic,* Amsterdam 1953, pp. 103f. – The solution represented by Prof. Moody is closely related to ours.

'P', name of a proposition, variable
'X', name of a proposition, constant
'WP' for 'P is true'
'MPp' for 'P means p in the sense of (a)'
'ZPp' for 'P means p in the sense of (b)'.
'WP', 'MPp' and 'ZPp' are propositions.
A new rule of substitution allows 'p' to be replaced by 'X'.
We use one definition (of falsity):

    1. FP = NWP

and three axioms from the propositional logic:

    2. CCpNpNp

    3. CCpKpNpNp

    4. CCpNKqrCpANqNr

As is manifest, *2* and *3* are formulations of the principle of the *reductio ad absurdum*; *4* is a form (falsity mode) of the laws attributed to De Morgan.

We turn now to the proof of the paradox of the 'Liar' as it reveals itself following interpretation (a). To this end, we set up the following special axioms:

    5. MXFX

    6. CMPpCWPp

    7. CMPpCFPNp

5 is a formulation of the 'Liar' paradox: it says that X (in the sense of (a)) means that X is false. *6* and *7* are (weakened) formulations of the Aristotelian definition of truth.[1]

6 asserts that if P means p, then if P is true, p is valid; and similarly, *7* says that if P means p, then if P is false, *not* − *p* is valid.

And the derivation follows:

        6 P/X, p/FX = C5 − 8

    8. CWXFX

        2 p/WX = C8 × 1 P/X − 9

    9. NWX

        9 × 1 P/X = 10

   10. FX

        7 P/X, p/FX = C5 − 11

---

[1] *CMPpEWPp* and *CMPpEFPNp* are the corresponding strong formulations.

11. *CFXNFX*

$$2\,p/FX = C11 - 12$$

12. *NFX*

But *12* stands in contradiction to *10*. The paradox is therefore derivable following interpretation (a). On the other hand, this is not so in the case of interpretation (b). We introduce here the following special axioms:

5'. *MXFX*

6'. *CMPpZPKWPp*

7'. *CZPpCWPp*

8'. *CZPpCFPNp*

5' is of the same form as 5. As opposed to this, 6' is new: it determines the meaning of 'Z' corresponding to our interpretation (b). 7' and 8' are, to be sure, analogous to 6 and 7. And now the derivation:

$$6'\,P/X, p/FX = C5' - 9'$$

9'. *ZXKWXFX*

$$7'\,P/X, p/KWXFX = C9' - 10'$$

10'. *CWXKWXFX*

$$3\,p/WX = C10' \times 1\,P/X - 11'$$

11'. *NWX*

$$11' \times 1\,P/X = 12'$$

12'. *FX*

$$8'\,P/X, p/KWXFX = C9' - 13'$$

13'. *CFXNKWXFX*

$$4\,p/FX, p/WX, r/FX = C13' - 14'$$

14'. *CFXANWXNFX*

$$14' \times 1\,P/X = 15'$$

15'. *CFXAFXNFX*

This is the only result which we obtain: If *P* is false, then *P* is false or *P* is not false; it does not contradict *12'*. On the contrary, if in 7' and 8' we had written an equivalence instead of an implication, then we would have obtained in the second part, just as in the first, a proof of the falsity of *P*. Noteworthy in this solution is the fact that it uses no metalanguage. To be sure, it is entirely metalinguistic (as is, indeed, nearly the entire Scholastic logic), but it is not the distinction of object language and metalanguage which constitutes the principle of solution here.

VI

I. M. BOCHENSKI

ON THE SYNTACTICAL CATEGORIES *

The theory of the syntactical categories (abridged here as 'SCs') has, since the twelfth century, been a traditional part of Scholastic logic. As a matter of fact we owe the idea to Aristotle.[1] After the barbarous period which for logic constitutes the modern centuries (sixteenth century–1847), the first new logicians showed hardly any interest in it. Husserl was the first to outline at the beginning of our century a sketch of a theory of SCs.[2] Nearly thirty years later, St. Leśniewski elaborated a rigorous system of it [3] – but the present author knows only of one general study on that subject in existence, a paper by Professor K. Ajdukiewicz.[4] It would seem that in spite of the brilliant development of other parts pertaining to the logical syntax, recent logicians are apt to neglect somewhat the problems of the SCs.[5]

And yet this subject is not entirely devoid of importance. Some of the confusions which are so often threatening to arise in logical systems,

---

* First published in *New Scholasticism* 23 (1949) 257–280.

[1] *On Interpretation* 1–5. 16a1–17a24. This is the first known attempt to classify the *SCs*; some remarks contained in that part of the works of Aristotle are still unsurpassed, e.g., the definition of a symbol, involved in 16a 2aff., the definition of a sentence, 17a 3ff. etc. There is no doubt that the Scholastics have greatly developed the Aristotelian syntax. But – as is generally the case in the entire domain of Scholastic logic – we have no information about it, since there does not exist a single satisfactory study on it.

[2] *Logische Untersuchungen* (Halle an der Salle, 1913) II, 294, pp. 305f; pp. 316f. pp. 326f. Husserl calls them 'Bedeutungskategorien' i.e., categories of meaning.

[3] *Grundzüge eines neuen Systems der Grundlagen der Mathematik*, Fundamenta Mathematicae, 11 (1929), 13f., 67f. It is unfortunate that St. Leśniewski (1885–1939) who was considered the most eminent Polish logician, died without having published more than a small part of the results of his research. Moreover, even those papers which have been published are seldom read or used.

[4] *Die syntaktische Konnexität*, Studia Philosophica, Commentarii Societatis Philosophicae Polonorum 1 (1935), pp. 1–28.

[5] The matter has been, of course, often mentioned and several definitions concerning it have been stated. Cf. e.g. A. Tarski, *Der Wahrheitsbegriff in den formalisierten Sprachen*, Studia Philosophica, 1, 261–406; R. Carnap, *Introduction to Semantics* (3rd ed., Cambridge, Mass., 1948), p. 43. Also the Grammarians have studied the subject, e.g. O. Petersen, *The Philosophy of Grammar* (London, 1924), pp. 961f.

might be avoided if some attention were paid to a doctrine of SCs. There is also no doubt that a doctrine of this nature would constitute a useful general framework for empirical investigations in linguistics and comparative grammar, and furthermore, it seems that the theory of SCs might have several rather important uses in ontology.[1]

The object of the present paper is to develop further the main ideas proposed by Professor Ajdukiewicz [2] by drawing a sketch of such a theory and applying it to some logical and ontological problems. The method will be a rather informal one; the reader is presumed to know the symbolism and the technique of elementary mathematical logic[3]; more complex notions will be shortly explained.

I.   THE THEORY OF THE SCs

There will be four sections in this part:
1. Definition
2. The principle of division
3. Division of the SCs
4. The SCs used in the *Principia Mathematica* *1–*34.

1. Definition

Alongside of the terms of logic we shall use here the following special primitive terms: 'symbol,' 'part', 'well formed formula', 'substitution';

---

[1] One may perhaps wonder how analyses of language may have any bearing on ontological problems. The answer – a part of what is said in part. II, section 2 of this paper – is, that there is an ontological background in any language: syntax mirrors ontology. This remark – which was suggested to the author by Professor E. W. Beth (to whom he is also indebted for several other suggestions and corrections) – seems to have rather important philosophic consequences. For, in view of our part. I, section 4 there can be no doubt that the ultimate background of the language of the *Principia Mathematica* is to be found in the same ontology which lies at the bottom of the current language – namely in the Aristotelian ontology – and the same again may said of all symbolic languages. We are not interested here in such problems; but the above remark may be offered to the students of Thomism as a subject for meditation.

[2] The main ideas explained in I, 1-3 and I, 1 are derived from this important paper, (quoted in footnote 4 on page 67). However, Professor Ajdukiewicz also speaks of semantical, not of syntactical categories; and for the formulation of the definitions and laws the author of the present paper is alone responsible.

[3] A. N. Whitehead and B. Russell: *Principia Mathematica*, I (2nd ed., Cambridge, 1935); W. Quine, *Mathematical Logic* (2nd ed., New York, 1947).

in the next chapter one more primitive term, 'determines', will be introduced. The intuitive explanation of the first four is the following:

'Symbol': x is a symbol of the language l – symbolically $Sy(x, l)$ – if and
only if (1) x is a written mark, (2) x is an element of l, (3) x has an
autonomous meaning in l – as opposed to such parts of symbols (e.g.
single letters) which do not mean anything alone in l.

'Part': x is a part of y in the language l – symbolically $P(x, y, l)$ – if and
only if (1) $Sy(x, l)$, (2) either $x = y$ or y is a series of symbols of l and x is
one of them.

'Well-formed formula' or, for the sake of brevity, *'formula':* z is a formula
of l – symbolically $Fl(x, l)$ – if and only if the parts of x are arranged in
x according to the syntactical laws of l and, consequently $Sy(x, l)$.

'Substitution': v is a substitution of y vor x in u – symbolically $Sb(x, y, u, v)$
– if and only if u and v have the same graphical form, except that everywhere x appears in u, y appears in v.

Our primitive terms being thus explained we may proceed to the formulation of the definition of the SC. We shall state it first in a verbal and still
inadequate form:

The symbols x and y belong to the same SC of the language l if and only
if, for every u and v, if $Sb(x, y, u, v)$ and $Fl(u, l)$ – then also $Fl(v, l)$ and
vice versa.[1]

Here are some instances drawn from the English language. The words
'logician' and 'ape' belong to the same SC of that language; for if
'every logician smokes a pipe' is a formula of the English language, then
'every ape smokes a pipe' is also a formula of it; and as 'every ape has a
tail' is a formula, so 'every logician has a tail' is a formula (in spite of the
first being, as far as the present writer knows, true and the second certainly
false: for both are meaningful, by the very fact that they are true or false;
no nonsense can be qualified by truth or untruth.) But 'logician' and
'eats' do not belong to the same SC: for 'every logician smokes a pipe'
is a foimula of the English language, while 'every eats smokes a pipe' is
not. This with apologies to the logicians.

[1] Contrary to Professor Ajdukiewicz (paper quoted in footnote 4 on page 67) we do not
mention the meaning in our definition; this presupposes that the language in question
is composed of non-ambiguous words. It might be shown, however, that even if the
words used were analogical, our definition would still remain correct. By eliminating
any mention of meaning, our definition becomes a purely syntactical one – which is an
advantage.

The above instances show that the classification of words by grammarians into nouns, verbs, adjectives, etc. is a division into SCs; it is however very badly done, without any kind of guiding principle and with a constant effort to accommodate the division to the diversity of natural verbal forms – an attempt which can no more succeed than that of a geometrician, who would try to establish a classification of geometrical forms by following the variety of shapes found in a living forest.

This being said, let us proceed to a more exact definition by means of logical symbols.

We must first of all define the (triadic) relation which holds between two symbols of a language when they can be mutually substituted in the above way. This relation is that of belonging to the same SC and will be symbolically denoted by 'SS':

(1) $SS(x, y, l) :: \equiv :: (u, v) :: Fl(u, l) :. \supset :. P(x, u, l) \cdot$
  $\cdot Sb(y, x, u, v) \cdot v \cdot P(y, u, l) \cdot Sb(x, y, u, v) : \supset : Fl(v, l)$

This is an exact statement of the description which was verbally given above; the apparent complication arises from the fact that we must provide for the mutual substitution of x for y and of y for x.

The relation which holds between a class of terms with the above characteristics and a language may be now defined; such class is a SC of that language. This relation will be denoted by 'SC':

(2) $SC(\alpha, l) \cdot \equiv \cdot (x, y) \cdot x, y, \varepsilon \alpha \supset SS(x, y, l)$

i.e.: α is a SC of l if and only if all elements of α can be mutually substituted in the above described way. We note that we did not define the generic notion of a SC, but only that of a SC of a given language – for only this is a useful notion. It would be, however, easy to define the SC quite generically: it is namely the class of all classes α such that for some l we have $SC(g, l)$ – i.e. it is the domain of SC.

A third relation must still be defined, namely the (triadic) relation which holds between a symbol, its SC and their language. We shall denote this relation by 'BS' which should indicate 'belongs to the SC'. The definition [1] runs as follows:

[1] As we are dealing with triadic relations, some notations of the logic of such relations (not contained in the *Principia*) will be used. We are reproducing them after R. Carnap, *Abriß der Logistik* (Vienna, 1929), pp. 43f., Bocheński-Menne, *Grundriß der Logistik*,

(3) $BS(x, \alpha, l) \cdot \equiv \cdot \alpha = sg'SC'(x, l)$

Finally, we shall use an abbreviation of the formula 'the second referent of BS in regard to x, l' i.e. 'the SC of x in l'; this will be denoted by 'CT' (x, l)':

$$CT = BS_2 .$$

The following laws, which can be easily derived from the above, are useful:

(4) $(l, x, y, u, v) :. Fl(u, l) \cdot P(x, u, l) \cdot Sb (y, x, u, v) \cdot \supset$
    $\supset \cdot Fl(v, l) : \supset : CT'(x, l) = CT'(y, l)$

i.e.: if two symbols may be mutually substituted in the described way, they belong to the same SC.

(5) $(l, x, y) : (\exists u, v) \cdot Fl(u, l) \cdot P(x, u, l) \cdot Sb(y, x, u, v) \cdot$
    $\sim \cdot Fl(v, l) \cdot \supset \cdot CT'(x, l) \neq CT'(y, l)$

i.e.: if there is a couple of sets of marks such that a substitution of y for x in one of them, which is a formula, gives as a result the other which is not a formula – then x and y do not belong to the same SC.

The following two laws are important:

(6) $(x, l): Sy(x, l) \cdot \supset \cdot (\exists \alpha) \cdot SC(\alpha, l) \cdot x \, \varepsilon \, \alpha$

i.e.: all symbols of a given language belong to a SC of that language.

(7) $(x, l): Fl(x, l) \cdot \supset \cdot (\exists \alpha) \cdot SC(\alpha, l) \cdot x \, \varepsilon \, \alpha$

i.e.: all formulae of a language belong to a SC of that language.

2. The principle of division

Each sentence is a whole and signifies as a whole. Consequently there can be only two alternative structures of a sentence: (1) either it is composed of one symbol only or (2) it is composed of more symbols and

---

2nd ed. Paderborn 1962, § 23. In a triadic relation we have three referents; there we shall have the notation 'R_1' (y, z)', 'R_2' (x, z)', 'R_3' (x, y)'. Similarly there will be three classes of referents, denoted, respectively, by '$sg_1'R'$ (y, z)', 'sg_2' R' (x, z)', 'sg_3' R' (x, y)'. Finally there is no converse domain, but three different domains: $D_1'R = \hat{x}$ (Ey, z) R (x, y, z), D_2' $(R = \hat{y}$ (Ex, z) R (x, y, z), D_3' $R = \hat{z}$ (Ex, y) R (x, y, z).

in that case there must be a connection between the symbols turning them into a meaningful whole. The question arises now as to the kind of that connection; and the answer is that it is always constituted by a determination of one or more symbols by another symbol. We define 'determines' as follows: the symbol x determines the symbol y if and only if what is meant by x is a property of what is meant by y – the word 'property' being understood in the widest possible sense, which includes essential factors, necessary and accidental properties and also relations. For if R is the name of a relation which holds between what is symbolized by x and y, we shall say that R determines x and y. This notion of determination is a very abstract one; it is, however, very useful, as we shall see. Now what is true of sentences applies also to all meaningful groups of symbols. In order that a group might be meaningful as a whole and not only a disconnected series of symbols, there must be a connection by determination; e.g. 'John, Peter' is meaningless and in order to supply it with a meaning we must add some determination, e.g. 'likes', 'and' etc. The justification of this fundamental principle of our theory of SCs is twofold: (1) We do not know – and even are unable to imagine – a language in which symbols would be connected in another way. (2) As the whole formula is meant to express an objective whole, the connection of symbols in a formula will necessarily follow, at least as far as the general principle is concerned, the mode of connection of parts in an object; now this connection is ultimately always the inherence of a property (in the widest sense of the word) in a subject. Some people seem to think that the inherence could be replaced by a material juxtaposition, like in the case of two stones placed one alongside the other. They forget that even in the case of our stones there is at least spatio-temporal relation between them and that it is absurd to consider that relation as a third stone located alongside of the two: it is in some way *in* the stones, it is a property of them.

If and only if x determines y, we shall say that x is an operator of y, and y the argument of x – symbolically $Op(x, y)$. The readers who are acquainted with mathematics are asked to forget here the mathematical meaning of the word 'operator' and to understand it exactly according to the above definition. There can be sometimes more than one argument of one operator – as in the case of relations: for in 'John likes the pipe' the operator 'likes' determines two arguments: 'John' and 'the pipe'. But the contrary is not possible: there can be only one operator directly determining one or more arguments. If more operators appear in the same formula, then they determine one another. E.g. in the sentence 'John is a very passionate smoker' the 'very' is the operator of 'passionate' and the group so formed ('very passionate') is the operator of 'smoker'; the whole 'very passionate smoker' is the (second) argument of the principal operator 'is'. The structure of that sentence becomes clear when we put all operators before their respective arguments and add parentheses. We obtain then:

$$\text{is } \{\text{John}, ([\text{very (passionate)}] \text{ (smoker)})\}$$

One remark may be added to these considerations. We used, in order to define the 'determines', a semantic, not a syntactical relation – and, as we did not develop a system of semantics, we were bound to state our definition in a rather vague form. This could be avoided by stating it in a purely syntactical way by saying e.g. that the operator is the symbol which precedes its argument, etc. This would require, however, a previous statement of a set of exact syntactical rules. Now no natural language and only few among the artificial languages possess such rules. It is therefore preferable, if we wish to study the laws of SCs in their generality, to abstain from a more rigorous definition and be content with the above description.

We may state now one important law of classification of SCs: whenever a symbol is an operator of another, the SC of the former is not identical with the SC of the latter:

(8) $(x, y, l) \cdot Op(x, y, l) \supset CT'(x, l) \neq CT'(y, l)$

This law is intuitive – but its main foundation is to be found in the fact that if it is violated antinomies result in the language.

3. Division of SCs

All symbols of any language fall into one of the following, mutually exclusive, classes

(1) $D'_1 Op \cap D'_2 Op$,

(2) $D'_1 Op \cap - D'_2 Op$,

(3) $- D'_1 Op \cap D'_2 Op$,

(4) $- D'_1 Op \cap - D'_2 Op$,   i.e.:

(1) symbols which are both operators and arguments,
(2) symbols which are operators but not arguments,
(3) symbols which are arguments but not operators,
(4) symbols which are neither operators nor arguments.

Out of these four classes, the first and third are abundantly represented in every language.

Symbols belonging to the third class will be called 'fundamental symbols' and their SCs 'fundamental SCs'; those symbols mean something which may have a property but cannot be a property. The symbols belonging to the first class will be shortly called 'operators' and their SCs 'operational SCs'; these symbols mean something which may both have a property and be a property.

The reason for admitting any determinate number of fundamental SCs must be an ontological or a conventional one; there is, it seems, nothing in the nature of the language as such which would prescribe it. There are, however, both ontological and semantical reasons to admit at least two fundamental SCs – and we know of no useful language which could be constructed without them. They are the SC of individual names – symbolically n – and that of sentences – symbolically s. We shall see later on that some more fundamental SCs seem to be necessary in a full language.

On the contrary, once certain fundamental SCs are admitted, a strictly determinated – but illimited – hierarchy of operational SCs is possible. One can, by a convention, limit their number – but not increase it. This hierarchy is built up by classifying the operators according to three criteria:

(1) the SC of their arguments,
(2) the number of their arguments,
(3) the SC of the whole formula, composed of the operator and its argument(s).

(1) An operator determining a symbol which belongs to the SC α will be called an 'α-operator'. The fundamental law is here that if $\alpha \neq \beta$ then an α-operator belongs to another SC than a β-operator:

(9) $(x, y, u, v, l): Op\ (x, u, l) \cdot Op(y, v, l) \cdot CT'(u, l) \neq$
$\neq CT'(v, l) \cdot \supset \cdot CT(x, l) \neq CT(y, l)$

74

According to this criterion all operation SCs may be divided into two classes (a) SCs of operators determining fundamental symbols; we shall call them 'F-operators'; (b) SCs of operators determining other operators; we shall call them 'O-operators'. The last class is that of the classical *syncategoremata*.

F-operators will be further divided according to the SC of the symbol they determine; thus we shall have name-operators, sentence-operators and so on – as many as there are fundamental SCs. The division of O-operators gives rise to a complex hierarchy. There will be first operators determining F-operators which will be called 'OF-operators'; then we shall have operators determining OF-operators: their name will be 'OOF-operators'; third, operators determining OOF-operators and so on, as far as needed.

(2) An operator may determine one or more arguments; and if $m \neq n$ the SC of an operator determining m arguments is different from that of an operator determining n arguments. In natural languages this rule is not observed. We say e.g. 'John smokes' (one argument of 'smokes') and 'John smokes a pipe' (two arguments). But by a closer consideration of the meaning of 'smokes' we see that either the first sentence is incomplete, or the meaning of 'smokes' is different in both cases. An operator determining n arguments will be called 'n-adic'. We shall thus have monadic, dyadic, triadic, tetradic, pentadic etc. operators.

(3) Finally, if $\alpha \neq \beta$, an operator which builds with its argument(s) a formula belonging to the SCα belongs to a different SC from an operator which builds with its argument(s) a formula belonging to the SCβ. An operator building with its argument(s) a formula of the SC will be called an 'α-building operator'. Consequently we shall have F-building, n-building, s-building, O-building, OF-building etc. operators.[1]

There exists a very useful notation for SCs of operators, which was

---

[1] A comparison of the above with the text of Petersen quoted in footnote 5 on page 67 might be instructive. The present article was already written, when the author read the highly interesting paper of Professor H. Curry, *Languages and formal systems*, Proceedings of the Xth International Congress of Philosophy, 1, Amsterdam 1949, 27–29, where similar ideas are briefly sketched and a convenient terminology is proposed. Professor Curry used 'functor' for our 'operator', 'operator' for 'name-building name-operator', 'predicator' for 'sentence-building name-operator', 'connector' for 'sentence-building sentence-operator'. It is characteristic that he does not quote the paper of Professor Ajdukiewicz; which seems to confirm our belief that this paper did not attract the attention it merited.

proposed by Professor Ajdukiewicz. An operational SC has been symbolized by a fraction whose numerator is constituted by the name of the
SC to which the formula it builds belongs, while the denominator is the
name(s) of the SC(s) of the symbol(s) it determines. If the latter are more
than one, two or more letters are written in the denominator, separated
by commas. Thus a name-building name-operator belongs to the SC n/n
if it is monadic; if it is dyadic, its SC will be $n/n, n$. An operator determining
a sentence-building sentence-operator and building with it another
sentence-building sentence-operator will belong to the SC

$$\frac{s/s}{s/s}$$

and so on.

Professor Ajdukiewicz uses this notation in order to establish a method
of verification to determine if a set of symbols is a well-formed formula.
The principle of this method is quite simple: if we write all operators
before their arguments and put under each the name of its SC, it is
enough to multiply these names, beginning at the right end, and to
remove the denominators. It is a formula if and only if the result is a
single name (a single letter of a single fraction). There are, however,
some special difficulties in treating quantifiers and some other symbols.
These were exhaustively examined by the author and we need not revert
to that matter here.

4. The SCs of the Principia Mathematica *1–*34

In order to illustrate our theory on one more extensive example, we shall
give here a short analysis of the first thirty-four paragraphs of the *Principia
Mathematica*; for we shall investigate to what SCs the symbols used in
that part of this work belong.

Let us note first that variables and their values belong evidently to the
same SC: for variables may be substituted by values. When speaking of
the 'range of values' the authors of the *Principia* meant classes which are
not without resemblance to the SCs: their notion is, however, rather vague.
For the theory of deduction (1*–5*) we find:

symbols: 'p', 'q', .. '$\sim$' 'v', '$\supset$', '$\cdot$', '$\equiv$'

SCs: s s/s $s/s, s$

The logic of propositions is, indeed, characterized by the fact that all its variables are elements of the SC of sentences, while all its operators are sentence-building sentence-operators. There are only two kinds of operators in that part of the *Principia*: monadic and dyadic; also there are no *O*-operators. It is clear, therefore, that the system of propositional logic contained in the work is only a very small section of the logic of propositions.

In the so-called theory of apparent variables (*9–*14) we find some name-operators. As to the fundamental symbols we have:

$$\text{symbols:} \underbrace{\text{'}a\text{', '}b\text{'} \ldots \text{'}x\text{', '}y\text{'} \ldots}_{n} \underbrace{\text{'}\phi\text{', '}\psi\text{'} \ldots}_{\substack{s/n \\ \text{or } s/n,\, n}} \underbrace{\text{'=', '}\neq\text{'}}_{s/n,\, n}$$

SCs

Thus it appears that the operators 'ϕ', 'ψ' etc. are ambiguous as to their SC: in *9–*10 they belong to the SC s/n, while in *11 they are elements of the SC $s/n, n$. In both cases they are sentence-building name-operators. Other symbols present some novelty. Thus, if we consider '$(\imath x)(\phi x)$' we find (1) that the 'ϕx' is an element of s; (2) that, nevertheless, the whole '$(\imath x)(\phi x)$' belongs to the SC n; consequently we see (3) that the prefix '$(\imath x)$' is an operator which, added to an element of s builds an element of n; it is a monadic name-building sentence-operator, i.e. belongs to the SC n/s.

The theory of classes brings some more and more radical novelties, namely a new fundamental SC to which belong the symbols of classes. It is the SC of universal names; let us denote it by 'u'. We shall see, analogically to the above analysis, that '$\hat{x}$', which, if added to '(ϕx)', builds a universal name, is a monadic universal-building sentence-operator, i.e. belongs to the SC u/s.

For other symbols of that part of the *Principia* we have:

$$\text{symbols:} \underbrace{\text{'}\alpha\text{', '}\beta\text{'} \ldots}_{u} \underbrace{\text{'}\varepsilon\text{' '}{-}\text{'}}_{s/n,\, u} \underbrace{\text{'}\cup\text{', '}\cap\text{'}}_{u/u} \underbrace{\text{'}\mathsf{C}\text{', '=', '}\neq\text{'}}_{s/u,\, u}$$

SCs:

The most interesting is the operator 'ε'. It is a dyadic operator, but each of its arguments belongs to a different SC: the first to n the second to u. One striking feature of the above table of symbols is that two of the operators corresponding to the four dyadic operators of the theory of deduction are universal-building and two sentence-building operators. All this shows how illogically the system was developed.

One remark about the symbol of existence. '$E!$' is evidently ambiguous: if it determines a description, it belongs to s/n; if it determines a class, to s/u; on the contrary '$\exists!$' is unambiguously an element of s/n.

The system of SCs of the logic of relations (*21, *23, *25, *30–*34) is the most complex. The symbols of relations themselves, 'R', 'S' etc., belong evidently to the SC $s/n, n$. When considering such symbols, the authors of the *Principia* propose to treat them in extension as names of classes of couples. But this is by no means necessary, and one can accomplish all operations indicated in the work while treating all symbols of (elementary) relations as elements of $s/n, n$, i.e. as operators. Thus for the symbols of the calculus of relations we have:

$$
\begin{array}{c|c|c|c|c}
\text{symbols:} & \text{'}R\text{', '}S\text{', } \ldots & \text{'}\dot{-}\text{'} & \text{'}\cup\text{', '}\cap\text{'} & \text{'}\subset\text{', '}\doteq\text{',} \\
\hline
\text{SCs:} & s/n, n & \dfrac{s/n, n}{s/n, n} & \dfrac{s/n, n}{s/n,n \ \ s/n,n} & \dfrac{s}{s/n,n \ s/n,n}
\end{array}
$$

The same remark applies here as to the calculus of classes. As to the '$\dot{\exists}!$' it belongs to the SC

$$\frac{s}{s/n,\, n}.$$

The determination of the SCs of symbols used in relative descriptions and similars is a little more complex. The 'Cnv'' and the '$\cup$' belong to

$$\frac{s/n,\, n}{s/n,\, n}.$$

But as 'Cnv' without the accent belongs to

$$\frac{s}{s/n, n \ \ s/n, n},$$

the accent alone will belong to

$$\frac{\dfrac{s/n,\, n}{s/n,\, n}}{\dfrac{s}{s/n, n \ \ s/n, n}}$$

If we consider now the individual descriptive functions, such as '$R'x$', we see that both the whole of that formula and the 'x' alone belong to n; consequently 'R'' is a name-building name-operator, i.e. belongs to n/n; but, as 'R' alone belongs to $s/n, n$, the accent which follows 'R' is an element of the SC

$$\frac{n/n}{s/n,\, n}.$$

A similar situation is found with the symbols of referents and relata. 'R' belongs, as we have seen, to n/n; but '$sg'R'$', '$gs'R'$' and the equivalent symbols with arrows belong, manifestly, to u/n, as they are universal-building name-operators. Consequently 'sg'', 'gs'' and the arrow alone which build with 'R'' elements of u/n belong to

$$\frac{u/n}{n/n}.$$

As, however, 'sg' and 'gs' belong to

$$\frac{s}{s/n,\, n \quad s/n,\, n}$$

the accent following them belongs to

$$\frac{\dfrac{u/n}{n/n}}{\dfrac{s}{s/n,\, n \quad s/n,\, n}}$$

It is, consequently, quite a different accent from the one which comes after 'R' and also from the accent which follows 'Cnv'.

The plural descriptive functions may be analyzed in a similar way; we shall limit ourselves to the remark that the double accent belongs to

$$\frac{u/u}{s/n,\, n}.$$

Finally the symbol of the relative product belongs manifestly to the SC

$$\frac{s/n,\, n}{s/n,\, n \quad s/n,\, n}.$$

The above analyses hold only if the functions named are atomic, i.e. if the ultimate arguments are elements of n. It is easy, however, to build up a hierarchy of SCs to which operators of non-atomic formulae would belong.

II. APPLICATIONS

We are now going to apply the doctrine of SCs to some logical and philosophical problems, namely to

1. The problem of antinomies,
2. The problem of univocity,
3. The problem of universals,
4. The problem of desiderative and imperative formulae.

1. The problem of antinomies

Some antinomies – namely the so-called 'logical' antinomies – may be resolved by a mere consideration of the SCs of the terms used: it will appear, consequently, that they are wrongly called 'logical' and are, as a matter of fact, purely syntactical.

(A) Let us consider first the well-known antinomy of the impredicable property. It may be stated as follows. We call 'impredicable' a property which is not a property of itself – as e.g. the property of being square which is itself by no means square. Let us write 'I' for 'impredicable'. We obtain thus

$$\text{(a)} \quad I(f) \equiv \sim f(f)$$

We substitute now 'I' for 'f' and obtain

$$\text{(b)} \quad I(I) \equiv \sim I(I)$$

which is said to be an antinomy.

But a simple consideration of the SCs of the terms shows that there is no antinomy, both formulas being nonsensical and the procedure of substitution incorrect. For '$f(f)$' is nonsensical, i.e. it is no well-formed formula. As a matter of fact, according to (8), the operator of an argument cannot belong to the same SC as its argument; thus the argument and the operator must have a different meaning – as terms with the same meaning can be mutually substituted, while terms belonging to different SC cannot; consequently, as the two 'f' in '$f(f)$' have the same meaning, the formula is nonsensical and is therefore not a sentence. Consequently, neither '$f(f)$', nor the whole of (a) – and similarly of (b) – are sentences, but nonsensical accumulations of symbols. Moreover, the substitution of 'I' for 'f' is illegitimate – as 'I' is an operator of 'f' in the left part of (a).

(B) Similar considerations will apply to the antinomy of classes. We define a class C as the class of classes which do not contain themselves as elements; we shall have thus:

(a) $\alpha \, \varepsilon \, C \equiv \, \sim (\alpha \, \varepsilon \, \alpha)$

by putting 'C' for 'α' we obtain

(b) $C \, \varepsilon \, C \equiv \, \sim (C \, \varepsilon \, C)$.

Now it has been shown by Professor Quine that the formula '$C \, \varepsilon \, C$' may be stated in the form of '$C(C)$', where the first 'C' is the operator of the second. Thus the same nonsense appears as in the antinomy of the impredicable property.

(C) On the contrary, the so-called 'semantical' antinomies cannot be solved by the mere consideration of the SCs of the terms as explained here. Let us take the antinomy of the heterologic word. It may be stated as follows. Let g be a property and G the name of g; the property of being heterologic will be represented by 'h', and the name 'heterologic' by 'H'. When we say that a word is heterologic we mean that its meaning is not a property of the word itself. We have thus:

(a) $h(G) \equiv \, \sim g(G)$

We now put 'H' for 'G' and 'h' for 'g' and obtain:

(b) $h(H) \equiv \, \sim h(H)$

which is an antinomy. Here, however, no breach of our rules of SCs is committed, for, in spite of 'g' being an operator, 'G' is a name; thus 'h' belongs to the SC s/n, and so does also 'g', but their names 'H' and 'G' are elements of n. Consequently, the substitution of 'H' for 'G' is a legitimate substitution of one name for another – and the substitution of 'h' for 'g' is also legitimate, as both are operators of the type s/n. It follows

81

that the theory of SCs, as stated by us, is not sufficient to resolve the so-called semantical antinomies.

The same could be exemplified in the antinomy of the 'liar' and many others.

The solution may be, however, easily obtained by introducing a new division of SCs according to the levels of languages; but as this part of syntax is well elaborated, we shall not enter into this matter.

2. *The problem of the univocity of being*

This is an ontological problem which may be stated in the following form: is there any property (in the widest sense of the word) common to all entities? It seems at first that *being* is such a property. One particular problem belonging to this group is that of univocity of being in regard to substances and accidents; there are, however, many other particular problems – as, for instance, the problem of univocity of being in regard to God and creature, etc. All these problems are very poignant to-day; it will suffice to recall that the celebrated French philosopher L. Lavelle holds the univocity of being in its generality, while Professor Karl Jaspers, the well-known existentialist, asserts that being is not univocal in regard to God and the creature. However, the way in which these problems are stated and discussed by philosophers today is very unsatisfactory, and one cannot help feeling that the cause for this state of affairs is to be found in a lack of a doctrine of SCs.

As a matter of fact there is a syntactical analogue of the problem of univocity. In order to demonstrate this, we shall limit our attention to one partial problem, namely that of univocity of being in regard to substance and accident.[1]

We must start with a description of what is meant by univocity. Strictly speaking, this is not a syntactical question, but belongs to semantics. Let us commence, therefore, with a description of the concept of meaning. We shall say that meaning is a (heterogeneous) tetradic relation: for if we have a meaning, there is always a symbol a, a language l, in which a means something, a thing x which a denotes and a property f which it connotes. This being the case, we shall write '$S(a, l, x, f)$'. Next let us

---

[1] For a more detailed treatment of univocity cf. I. M. Bocheński, *On Analogy*, in this book pp. 97f.

note that univocity is a relation existing between two words of the same language and that these words must have the same graphical form. The relation of univocity is therefore a heptadic relation between two words, one language, two things and two properties; the things are distinct and the properties are, of course, identical. Thus the definition of univocity may be stated in the following terms, where '$Is(a, b)$' means that a and b have the same graphical form:

(10) $Un(a, b, l, x, y, f, g) \cdot \equiv \cdot S(a, l, x, f) \cdot S(b, l, y, g) \cdot$
$\cdot Is(a, b) \cdot x \neq y \cdot f = g$.

For our present needs a partial relation contained in Un will be sufficient, namely the triadic relation $Univ$ which will be defined as follows [1]:

(11) $Univ(a, b, l) \cdot \equiv \cdot (x, y, f, g) \cdot S(a, l, x, f) \cdot$
$\cdot S(b, l, y, g), Is(a, b) \cdot x \neq y \cdot f = g$.

While considering (11) we see that univocal symbols must belong to the same SC: for they have the same graphical form and the same meaning; consequently they can be mutually substituted in a formula without causing that formula the loss of the character of a well-formed formula; now this is a sufficient condition for belonging to the same SC, according to (4). We can put then:

(12) $(a, b, l) : Univ(a, b, l) \cdot \supset \cdot CT'(a, l) = CT'(b, l)$.

The second thing we must do, is to show how a syntactical situation corresponds to an ontological one. This is easily done as far as our partial problem is concerned. For if f is an accident of a then 'f' will be an operator of 'a'. Generically, the symbols of substances must be names and symbols of accidents must be operators. It might be objected that accidents are often denoted by names – as is the case when we use so-called abstract words, as 'goodness', 'science' etc. But this is not opposed to our assertion – only the word 'name' is ambiguously used. As a matter of fact, according to our theory of SCs, a name is always a fundamental symbol, i.e. a symbol of something which may have properties but cannot be a property. Now the abstract words, quoted above, mean accidents, i.e. something which not only can, but even must, be a property of

[1] See footnote on page 82.

something else. Thus even the abstract 'names' of accidents are operators according to our terminology. It appears thus that the SC of the symbol of a substance is always different from that of an accident. We can even say that the opposition of fundamental symbols to operators is a syntactical counterpart of the ontological opposition of substance and accident.

In view of this statement it is easy to see that the doctrine of univocity of being is, as far as our problem is concerned, false. For if a be a name, b its operator and B_1 and B_2 two 'being' such that $Op(B_1, a, l)$ and $Op(B_2, b, l)$, according to (8), the SCs of B_1 and B_2 must be different. But if the doctrine of univocity of being be true, B_1 and B_2 must be univocal and thus, by (12) belong to the same SC. Consequently the doctrine of univocity of being is not true, i.e. it is false.

To this argument two objections may be raised.

(1) The partisans of the doctrine of univocity may say that they are not interested in SCs, which are a matter of speech, but in the ontological situation. To that, however, we answer that they cannot, in any way, *speak* while using univocally the word 'being' without violating the fundamental principles of syntax.

(2) It may also be objected that another system of SCs is perhaps possible; and such system would perhaps allow F-operators and O-operators to belong to the same SC. But *quod gratis affirmatur, gratis negatur:* We never heard of such a system nor of any correct language built in contradiction to our principles; moreover we do not see how antinomies could be avoided in a system without our (8). If the supporters of univocity are able to propose such a system, the present writer would gladly acknowledge his mistake; however, it must not be a vague accumulation of words, so common in the writings of philosophers, but a real system put forward in precise and clear terminology.

3. *The problem of universals*

Some contemporary nominalists endeavor to show that it is possible to construct a complete system of logic without using any universals. This is certainly not the case with the system of the *Principia* where, as we have already seen, symbols of classes are elements of the SC of universal

84

names. We already noticed, however, that the formulae of the *Principia* may be restated in such a manner as to dispense with that category. It suffices, in fact, to substitute '$a(x)$' for '$x \, \varepsilon \, \alpha$' and to expand all formulas such as '$\alpha \subset \beta$' etc. in order to eliminate all universal names. In this manner some writers believe that they have established the nominalistic thesis: for *entia non sunt multiplicanda praeter necessitatem,* and there appears to be no necessity to use universal symbols.

This conclusion seems to be hardly justified, since it can be objected that a universal symbol does not need to be a name – it is enough that it be an operator. Now all operators used in contemporary logic (as also in other sciences) are, evidently, universal operators. Even 'an individual operator' appears to be nonsense. The present writer is, moreover, of the opinion that the classical moderate realists – e.g. Aristotle and St. Thomas Aquinas – denied that there were universal things or real subjects: they even say explicitly that the so-called 'second' i.e. universal substance is a quality which, if translated into a syntactical language, means that the verbal universals are always operators, not names. But this opinion is not commonly received among Thomists. In any way it seems that Platonists must defend the existence of universal names; and even in traditional Scholastic teaching there are some chapters, e.g. the celebrated 'tree' of Porphyry, which can hardly be correctly analyzed without the use of universal names.

Some nominalists go farther than the first named position. They assert, in fact, that there cannot be any universal names and try to prove it by means of regular syntactical demonstrations. It has been shown, however, that these demonstrations proceed on the assumption that there are only two fundamental SCs: that of sentences and that of individual names, which is, of course, an intolerant assumption and causes the demonstration to be a *petitio principii.*

It is therefore necessary to state that there is nothing in the theory of SCs which would prevent any expansion of the system by introducing new SCs; and, among others, the SC of universal names may be introduced, should anybody wish to do so. The problem cannot, consequently, be solved on this ground – and both parties must offer some logical or ontological reasons in support of their assertions. We may only note that the Platonists, and such Thomists who do not admit the above considerations, are by no means short of arguments; especially as to the application

85

of the razor of Ockham they would retort that it cuts not only unnecessary entities, but also a part of reality.[1]

4. The problem of desiderative and imperative formulae

This is a problem very similar to that of the universals, as in that case also many thinkers try to analyze desiderative and imperative formulae – such as 'I wish to smoke' or 'Do not smoke!' – by means of the usual two SCs of names and sentences only. The only difference is that here the reduction is far more difficult. The present writer – who, however, does not wish to take up a position here as to the philosophical problem itself – is under the impression that all efforts to analyze desiderative and imperative formulae in this manner completely fail to do justice to their meaning.

As a matter of fact the 'to smoke' is not a sentence, for it is neither true nor false. Nor is it a name, as names are symbols of things and no such thing as *to smoke* exists, nor can exist. And if it is said that the formula means 'When I shall have my pipe lit I shall be satisfied', then it is quite clearly a misinterpretation of the original sentence; the same must be said about the other current interpretation 'When I do not smoke, I feel discomfort' – for to feel discomfort is one thing, and to wish another, quite different thing. The situation with imperatives is similar. It is not true that 'Do not smoke!' means: 'If you will smoke I shall get angry'; nor are the other interpretations in terms of the SCs of names and sentences – at least those which are known to the present writer – any better.

Moreover there are at least two arguments in favour of the assertion that such reduction is impossible. For, first of all, these desiderative and imperative formulae are far too common to natural languages and far

---

[1] The most significant recent studies in the problem of universals known to the author are: W. Quine, *On universals*, The Journal of Symbolic Logic 12 (1947), 74–83; N. Goodman and W. Quine, *Steps toward constructive nominalism*, ibid., 105–122 (the last named has, in spite of its title, nothing to do with nominalism as traditionally understood: the position of the authors is simply anti-Platonic); A. Paas, *A semantic examination of realism*, The Journal of Philosophy 44 (1947), 561f. (a brilliant defense of a realistic position). The main ideas expounded in this paragraph are due, however, to Professor K. Ajdukiewicz's (Polish) paper on universals, The Journal of Symbolic Logic, 1 (1936), n. 225, 10. See also in this book *On Analogy*, p. 97 and *The Problem of Universals*, p. 118.

too clearly opposed to sentences of the usual type, for this is to be attributed to historical accidents. Not even the cases in a declension are accidental, but each of them has a logical foundation. Secondly, when analyzing the meaning of our formulae we see clearly enough that they possess a particular structure which seems to be quite different from that of sentences or names.

One curious feature of these formulae is, in fact, that they all contain – more or less explicitly – a sentence as a part of them. Thus 'I wish to smoke', when expanded, becomes: 'I wish that I smoke'; and 'Do not smoke' becomes 'It is a law (obligation, norm, etc.) that you do not smoke.' They are sentences qualified by a peculiar operator which builds with them a new SC. According to the terminology used by St. Thomas Aquinas we shall call such formulae 'enuntiables' and the corresponding SC will be denoted by 'e'. Based on this assumption we get the following analysis of the sentence: 'I wish that I smoke':

$$\text{wish} \ \{\text{I}, (\text{that } [\text{smoke } \langle \text{I} \rangle]) \}$$
$$s/n, e \quad n \quad e/s \quad s/n \quad n$$

VII

ALBERT MENNE

THE LOGICAL ANALYSIS OF EXISTENCE *

Besides 'existentialism' whose elaboration of existence often represents, to be sure, absurd poetry of uncontrollably high standard, the neo-positivistic 'Vienna Circle' and the analytic school of philosophy prevalent in England and America have also been concerned with 'existence'. All these inquiries are based upon the existence concept of the *Principia Mathematica* of Whitehead and Russell.[1] This comes about in the following way: If in connection with Gottlob Frege one considers a proposition such as, for example, 'the rose is red' as being composed of the predicate 'is red' and the argument 'the rose', then such a sentence possesses the form '$f(a)$' in which 'f' would symbolize a predicate of one digit and 'a' a determinate individual. In place of the symbol for a determinate, constant individual, it is possible to leave the space empty, thus obtaining the propositional form '$f(\ )$' from the proposition. In order to emphasize the fact that something can be put into the empty space between the parentheses, it is also written '$f(x)$'. This variable [2] 'x' means nothing at all in itself but only indicates the place in which a constant can be put. Through such a substitution of a constant for a variable, a proposition again results from the propositional form. If, for example, 'f' denotes 'is red', 'b' 'the tomato' and 'c' 'the lemon', then '$f(b)$' results in the true proposition 'the tomato is red' and '$f(c)$' in the false proposition, 'the lemon is red'.

However, there is still a second possible way to convert a proposition: one binds the variable by means of a quantifier.[3] '$\forall x$' in this manner designates the generalizator in which '$\forall$' has approximately the meaning of 'all'. '$\forall x f(x)$' then means 'for all $x, f(x)$', that is, 'all x are f'. If 'f'

---

* Lecture held on December 11, 1958 at the University of Hamburg.
[1] A. N. Whitehead and B. Russell, *Principia Mathematica,* Cambridge, I 1910, II 1912, III 1913, 3rd edition 1950.
[2] The discoverer of the variable is Aristotle.
[3] Quantifiers, to be sure, are found for the first in Albert of Sachsen. Contemporary theory goes back to G. Frege.

means, for example, 'is identical with itself', then $'\forall x f(x)'$ means 'all things are identical with themselves'.

In the particularizator $'\exists x'$, the $'\exists'$ means 'some' in the sense of 'at least one'; $'\exists x f(x)'$ corresponds to 'for at least one $x, f(x)$', that is 'some x are f'. If $'f'$ means 'is red', then $'\exists x f(x)'$ means 'some things are red'. One can also interpret the particularizator $'\exists x'$ by: 'there is an x for which...' or 'there exists an x such that...' and therefore the particularizator is also called the existence operator. The designation is not entirely fortunate for the generalizator or all-operator naturally asserts existence also. Every quantification of a propositional form asserts that the corresponding predicate is valid for one existing individual or for all existing individuals – unless it be that we are in an absolutely empty world. And then neither generalizator nor particularizator could signify existence.

Existence of descriptions and classes introduced later in the *Principia Mathematica* is defined in both cases with the help of the particularizator. The symbols 'E!' and '∃!' therefore represent nothing new in principle but are simply abbreviations.

'Existence' thus appears in the current logical calculi, which are based upon the *Principia Mathematica,* only as an existence operator and this is always a functor of second degree [1] with a predicator as argument. 'Existence' in this sense is not a property like other properties but one can speak meaningfully only of the existence of an object of which a property is at the same time exhibited. Now the neopositivists, from the obvious facts that the meaning of particularizator as existence operator furnishes us with an existence concept to whose use are to be attributed only finite claims, have drawn the conclusion that 'existence' may be used *only* in this sense and that every other use evokes logical confusion and that therefore every autonomous application of 'existing' independent of a determinate property or even the treatment of existing itself as a property is entirely senseless. [2]

Hugo Bergmann, among others, has energetically attacked these assertions. After a fundamental analysis of the concept of existence, he comes to

---

[1] This accounts for the syntactical properties of existence operators and its relations to the universal operator. Compare A. Menne, *Zur Stufenkoppelung monadischer bivalenter Funktoren,* Kontrolliertes Denken, München 1951, pp. 92f.

[2] Because of this it would be very easy to do away with the so-called 'ontological proof' of Anselm of Canterbury since here 'existence' is compared with other properties and because of this God is associated with a predicate. See Anselm's *Proslogion,* Part II.

the conclusion: 'After all that has been said, we must adhere to this, namely, that the claims of some logicians to have explained the concept of existence entirely by means of that concept of existence common in mathematical logic and their assertion that all other meanings of existence can either be derived from this concept or rest on confusion, represents an unjust exaggeration. The connection of an existence concept with a predicate and the corresponding propositional function, although in many cases it may be correct, does not *exhaust* the essence of the existence concept.' [1] The following exposition will now attempt to accommodate this critique. It will be shown that a logical analysis of the concept of existence which is not at the outset undertaken with the existence operator as the point of departure offers a satisfactory result which, among other things, also produces an answer to the problem of universals.

The many strata of the concept of existence are easily discernible if we ask something about the existence of the Cathedral of Cologne, of a prime number between 35 and 40, of a class that is equal to the complement of its complement, of the wife of Zeus, of the robber Karl Moor. It is a rough simplification to attribute existence only to that which one can touch and to declare everything else a fiction; for among these 'fictions' to which belongs all of mathematics [2], is to be found the aforementioned prime number between 35 and 40 whose mathematical existence is incontestable simply by allusion to the number 37, as well as an elementary method of division of an angle into three equal parts which actually represents a fiction since its impossibility was proved in 1837 by Wantzel. Whether we acknowledge the existence of the objects enumerated above certainly depends entirely upon which domain of objects, which 'universe of discourse', we make the foundation of our consideration; that is, we can attribute existence to every one of the above mentioned objects if we at any given time mean thereby real, respectively, mathematical, logical, mythical, poetic existence. But to something impossible such as the elementary and at the same time exact division of an angle into three equal parts, the squaring of circles or a city which lies north of itself one can meaningfully attribute no existence unless one associates existence with the domain

---

[1] Hugo Bergmann, *Probleme des Existenzbegriffes*, Theoria (Lund 1950), XVI/1, 33.
[2] B. v. Freytag-Lörringhoff actually asserts in *Gedanken zur Philosophie der Mathematik*, Meisenheim 1948, that the object of mathematics are fictions like the Little Red Riding Hood of the fairy tale!

of the null class which is a suitable definition of the domain of the non-existent, then 'existing in the null class' says the same as 'not existing'.

How many such kinds of existence there are cannot be determined *a priori,* Empirical and ontological grounds could bring about the further distinction or union of domains of being. Thus, for example, reasons could be given for further dividing the domain of the real-existent into a domain of physical, biological and psychical phenomena to which then belongs a special form of existence.

Two domains occupy an exceptional position here: that of the real to which we commonly refer in everyday language as 'existing'. (A merchant who inquires about the capacities of a business partner is interested in the actual existence of these properties, not in wishes and phantasies; and whoever inquires about the existence of God naturally seeks not the mythical, but rather the real existence of God.) That the domain of the real is marked out has inner, ontological reasons. On the other hand, the domain of the logical is distinguished on formal grounds as we shall see further on.

If we now fix upon a determinate domain of objects as a 'universe of discourse', then 'existence' can be used here in the sense of the *Principia Mathematica,* that is, existing means as occurring as argument of a function, for example,

$$\exists\, x \; \{\text{situated in Cologne}\}\,(x) \wedge \{\text{cathedral}\}\,(x)\,,$$

that is, 'there is a Cologne Cathedral'.

Existence thus can be asserted only of the argument of a predicate or of a symbol or of a class, and not, on the other hand, of an individual only exhibited or named and by no means of a variable as a designation for a completely indeterminate thing. That is the existence concept about as Juhos [1] has analyzed it. It is also the existence concept that Bergmann has analytically derived from the *Principia Mathematica* and which he designates as that not *alone* valid, as pointed out above. That becomes clear at once if the proposition which results states to which object domain an individual in general belongs, that is, in what sense it exists.

This inquiry itself naturally does not belong to logic but is a concern of

---

[1] Béla Juhos, *The Application of Logical Analysis to Philosophical Problems*, Methodos, Milano 1951, 81f., and the *Analytical Method*, Zeitschrift für philosophische Forschung, VI/I, 1951, 42f.

ontology. As a consequence, propositions result which associate an element with a class and are therefore of the form:

$$a \; \varepsilon \; \text{Cls}$$

for example: (Cologne Cathedral) ε [real] ,

that is 'the Cologne Cathedral belongs to the domain of real objects'; in other words, 'the Cologne Cathedral exists really'. While existence in the first sense (which we shall call formal existence) appears in the calculus as an operator (and indeed always as operator on a predicate, on a class or on a symbol and so as an operator of the second order [1], existence is encountered in the second sense (which we shall term ontological existence) chiefly in the determination of the 'universe of discourse', that is, in talking about the calculus, and so has a metalogical character. But of course the metalogic can also be formalized and then predicates corresponding to the individual domains of objects result and these predicates designate the membership of the actual domain of objects. The predicates, for example, 'really existing' are in the calculus functors of the first order and therefore have individuals as arguments; for example,

$$\{\text{really existent}\} \text{ (Caesar)},$$

that is, 'Caesar exists really'.

$$\{\text{mythically existent}\} \text{ (Zeus)},$$

that is, 'Zeus exists mythically'.

With only the help of the concept of existence one can by no means destroy the so-called 'ontological proof of God' of Anselm of Canterbury. He distinguishes [2] 'esse in re' and 'esse in solo intellectu' and so one can construct quite correctly ' {really existent} (God)' and ' {purely intellectually existent} (God)'. In so far as one acknowledges Anselm's further presuppositions that 'really existing' is greater than 'pure intellectually existing' and that the greatest predicate must apply to God then the concept 'God' necessarily possesses also the characteristic of the concept {really existent}. Of course, whether from a concept which contains real existence as a characteristic one may strictly imply the real existence of an object corresponding to the concept is another question that can be decided only within a certain epistemological position.

---

[1] Compare footnote 1 on page 89.
[2] Anselm of Canterbury, *Proslogion*, Chapt. II.

Existence thus becomes something relative and disintegrates into many modes. In order to obtain a uniform and general concept of existence, could one add the mode of existing as an attribute to the argument and then ask accordingly: 'Does the real Caesar exist?', respectively, 'Does the mythical Zeus exist?' The formalized answers read as follows:

$$\{\text{existent}\} \text{ (real Caesar)}$$
$$\{\text{existent}\} \text{ (mythical Zeus)}$$

But that could also have been written with the existence operator:

$$\exists\, x.\ \{\text{real}\}\ (x) \land x \equiv \text{(Caesar)}\,.$$

With that, we are again back to the existence concept of the first sense. The predicate, without which the existence operator cannot be meaningfully applied, reveals itself here through the mode of existence which becomes in this case an intensional predicate corresponding, for example, to the redness of the rose. Every special mode of ontological existence can be represented thus by means of the formal existence operator and an intensional predicate. Formal existence is therefore a general concept and accordingly a presupposition of ontological existence; ontological existence is constructed from the former and from an intensional determination; in other words, ontological problems of existence can be decided only intensionally and not in a purely formal-logical way.

One can go still a step further: even if the mode of ontological existence is completely unknown, existence propositions somewhat of the form 'Caesar exists' can be formed without contradicting the rules of use of the existence operator. To 'Caesar' is added simply the predicate 'called Caesar' and then there results:

$$\exists\, x\ \{\text{called Caesar}\}\ (x)\,.$$

Without naming a thing in any way, one cannot properly speak of it; since a predicator can in principle always be constructed from this naming, existence can also be asserted of everything of which one speaks. With that the question remains quite open as to whether such an assertion of existence represents a true or a false proposition.

Of the thing in itself, which Johus believes to be able to remove through a mere analysis of the existence concept [1], since it is still wholly in accord with the use of the existence operator, it is valid to say:

[1] Zeitschrift für philosophische Forschung VI/1, 1951, 46; Methodos (1951) 89; compare footnote 1, p. 91.

93

$$\exists\, x\, \{\text{being in itself}\}\,(x)$$

But whether the property 'being in itself' is meaningful and whether there is anything which bears this property is a problem of ontology and must be decided by it.

Now, what in general does the formal concept of existence say? It is the merit of Ivo Thomas [1] to have pointed out with emphasis that all forms of existence propositions of *Principia Mathematica* are always equivalent with an assertion that a certain class is not equal to the null class.

$$\exists\, x \cdot f(x) : \leftrightarrow \cdot \hat{x} f(x) \neq \dot{O}$$

The null class on the other hand is equal to the domain of objects which are not identical to themselves, that is, objects which are contradictory:

$$\dot{O} = \hat{x}\,(x \neq x)\,.$$

Existence propositions are therefore equivalent to the proposition that a given class is not contradictory; in other words, formal existence signifies nothing more than freedom from contradiction. In the logical calculus of the *Principia Mathematica,* existence can appear explicitly only as formal existence and so is called freedom from contradiction. Unfortunately, Russell's examples are often very misleading and capable of concealing these facts. For example unicorns are non-existent only in relation to the domain of real objects. But they are in no way contradictory in themselves and therefore certainly possess logical existence. On that account they are completely unsuitable as an example of a null class. Such examples can therefore not be introduced [2] as counter instances to the 'contested' rule *'Darapti',* etc. and to the law of sub-alternation, as is so often done.

That the formal existence of logic signifies only formal freedom from contradiction establishes in its exceptional position in relation all other modes of existence. It forms for these a necessary presupposition, although the above existence concepts always contain in addition an extra-logical, intensional component. They are, as all other classes and predicates,

---

[1] Ivo Thomas, *Existence and Coherence*, Methodos II/5, 1950, 76f.
[2] A detailed examination of the importance of existence for syllogistic is to be found in A. Menne, *Logik und Existenz,* Meisenheim 1954. A distinguished condensation of this is presented in: J. Dopp, *Une formalisation de la logique traditionelle des propositions générales, due à M. Menne,* Revue philosophique de Louvain, 53 (1955) 566–96.

subject to the rules of logic but they represent no concepts of *the* logic; rather they are extra-logical determinations.

In the sense of the logicism of Russell and Frege who desire to construct mathematics solely from logic, logical and mathematical existence coincide. Since the logical calculus of *Principia Mathematica* is indeed primarily meant to serve in the construction of mathematics, the fact that only the concept of logical existence found a place in it is accounted for.

In conclusion, let us take up still a further, often discussed, problem: What is the situation with regard to the existence of universals? First of all, one should once and for all make a clear distinction between purely logical classes that are revealed as extensions of corresponding predicates and real objects, such as cats, trees or chairs which can be collected into groups on the basis of common characteristics.

The existence of a class is of a purely logical form; it is certainly to be distinguished from the existence of its elements. There results correspondingly: an object exists logically if the extension belonging to the predicates is not empty; in other words, if it possesses no contradictory properties. Entirely analogously, then, a class exists precisely if its properties (that are not to be confused with the properties of its elements!) are not contradictory. To be sure, there exists no object which could be the element of a null class, for such an object would indeed be contradictory in itself. But the null class does exist if the property 'possesses no element' is not contradictory in itself. Without detriment to type theory, therefore, existence as formal, logical existence belongs to classes. The existence of a group of trees, on the other hand, is just as real as are the individual trees: existence of no kind belongs to the group independent of the objects of which it consists (Conceptualism at best veils the facts if it means that in the consciousness a special existence belongs to the group: existence of the group in consciousness exists in so far as the individual trees have existence in consciousness. If these exist only in consciousness, then the group also has no other existence; but if the trees are real and are collected into a group on the basis of a real quality, then this group is also real, but not, naturally, independent of its parts.) The inclusion of several things in a group occurs on the basis of a common property. Trees, for example, are included in a group on the basis of their similar leaf forms and fruit or because of being found in a certain vicinity. One can now interpret this common mark as a predicate; the extension of this then results in a class that corresponds to the original group. Furthermore, to such a class naturally belongs logical existence and, this is true, even though there is no real existence of the group and its trees or the real existence of the group and its trees no longer continues. On the other hand, the real group possesses existence that is in wo way independent of the trees which make up the group. To be sure, a logical factor plays a part in the construction of groups: the individual trees are real and the properties which they possess also are thoroughly real. Nevertheless, the agreement (respectively equality or similarity) of properties represents a logical relation which itself does not exist really if it also exists *cum fundamento in re*.

That one can describe the formally existing classes by means of real groups is not so astonishing. As we saw, real existence always presupposes logical existence; thus logical existence is contained in the real existence of the group. Incompatible with this view is a nominalism which declares all universals and classes to be purely arbitrary products of the human being. As opposed to this, Platonism is confirmed with reference to classes to which belongs a special, formal existence and Aristotelianism is confirmed with reference to the group which can exist only through its parts.

Therefore, in conclusion it may be said:

1. Formal existence signifies freedom from contradiction.
2. Formal existence is not the only mode of existence. There are many more forms of ontological existence in addition to those intensionally determined, and certainly at least as many modes as there are classifications of being.
3. Ontological existence always assumes formal existence.
4. A mere analysis of the concepts of existence does not suffice to reduce problems such as the 'ontological proof of God' or the 'thing in itself' *ad absurdum*.
5. With reference to the problem of universals, a certain Platonism can be justified for the domain of logic without detriment to the Aristotelian solution with reference to real things.

VIII

I. M. BOCHENSKI

ON ANALOGY *

1. Introductory

The present paper is an attempt to clear up some of the problems involved in the traditional theory of analogy as presented by the Thomistic school. The two main ideas behind the formal developments offered here are (1) analogy is an important discovery, worthy of a thorough examination and further development, (2) contemporary mathematical logic supplies excellent tools for such work. This paper is, as far as the author knows, the first of its kind[1]; it deals with a difficult subject in a sketchy way; what it contains is, therefore, not meant to be definitive truths, but rather proposals for discussion.

The approach to the problems of analogy used here is the semantic one. This is not the only method, but it would seem to be both the most convenient and the most traditional. As a matter of fact, it is difficult to see how equivocity, which is and must be treated as a relation of the same type as analogy, can be considered except by the semantic method. Also, St. Thomas Aquinas examined analogy in his question concerning divine names and the title of Cajetan's classical work is *De Nominum Analogia*. It will be taken for granted that the reader has a good knowledge of classical texts of St. Thomas and Cajetan, and of the content of the *Principia Mathematica*[2]; no reference will be made to these works, except

---

* First published in *The Thomist* 11 (1948) 474–497.
[1] The author is, however, indebted to the late Fr. Jan Salamucha and to J. Fr. Drewnowski who were the first to apply recent formal logic to Thomistic problems. The present paper may be considered as an attempt to formalize some of the opinions expressed by them. Cf. *Myśl katolicka wobec Logiki współczesnej* (Polish = The Catholic thought and contemporary logic), Poznan 1937 (with French abstracts) and J. Fr. Drewnowski, *Zarys programu filozoficznego* (Polish = A sketch of a philosophic programme), Przegląd Filozoficzny, 37, 1943, 3–38, 150–181, 262–292, especially 95–98. (There is a French account of this important work in Studia Philosophica (Lwów) I, 1935, 451–454.
[2] A. N. Whitehead and B. Russell, *Principia Mathematica*, 2nd ed., Cambridge 1925–1927.

for some laws used in the proofs. Other more recent topics of mathematical logic needed for the theory, as, e.g., plural relations[1], semantics[2], etc., will be explained.

The main results of our inquiry are: (1) an exact definition of univocity, equivocity, and analogy of attribution; (2) proof of the principles of contradiction and of excluded middle for univocal and equivocal names; (3) a metalogical examination and exact translation of the formula 'analogy itself is analogical'; (4) proof that a syllogism in *Barbara* with analogical middle terms, if analogy is defined according to the alternative theory, is a correct formula; (5) criticism of the alternative theory; (6) definition of analogy of proportionality by isomorphy; (7) proof that a syllogism in *Barbara* with analogical middle terms, if analogy is explained according to the isomorphic theory, is a correct formula; (8) a suggestion that contemporary logic uses analogy.

Incidentally other results are reached, which may have a more general relevance: (1) the foundations of a semantic system, useful for Thomistic logic, are sketched; (2) a generalised table of relevant semantic relations between two names is given; (3) the formal validity of a syllogism in *Barbara,* as opposed to its verbal correctness, is defined; (4) a rudimentary analysis of causality, as understood by Thomists, is supplied.

2. *Meaning*

The fundamental notion of our theory is that of meaning, described by the following formula: 'the name a means in the language l the content f of the thing x' (symbolically: '$S(a, l, f, x)$'.) The situation symbolized by '$S(a, l, f, x)$' will be called a 'semantic complex'. In spite of its simplicity the semantic complex merits a detailed comment.

(1) By 'name' we understand here a written word or other written symbol. It must be emphasized that a written symbol is just a black mark (a spot of dry ink) on paper. As such (*materialiter sumptum*) it is a physical object which occupies a given position in space and time. It may happen, therefore, that two names, e.g., a and b have the same graphical form (symbolically $I(a, b)$, where 'I' suggests 'isomorphy') but we cannot

---

[1] Cf. R. Carnap, *Abriß der Logistik*, Wien 1929, pp. 43–45; Bocheński-Menne, *Grundriß der Logistik*, 2nd ed., Paderborn 1962, § 23.

[2] Cf. A. Tarski, *Der Wahrheitsbegriff in den formalisierten Sprachen*, Studia Philosophica (Lwów), I, 1935, 261–405.

speak correctly of 'the same' name which occurs twice, e.g. as middle term in a syllogism. In that case we have always two different names of the same graphical form.

(2) Every relation of meaning implies a reference to a language. This is obvious, for the same name may mean one thing in one language and something quite different in another. Moreover, it may have no meaning at all in another language. If the mention of a language is omitted in classical definitions, it is because the authors writing during the Middle Ages and the Renaissance thought of the only one language used at that time, Latin.

(3) What we call 'content' is what classical Thomists called *'ratio'*. This *ratio* is always conceived as something determining the thing whose content it is; even in case of substantial contents (as 'substance' and similars) we conceive them as such and St. Thomas explicitly teaches that in this case we always have to do with a quality in a broader meaning (including 'substantial quality')

(4) Finally, the 'thing' means the same as the *'res'* of the Thomists, namely the subject to which the content connoted by the name belongs. This is, at least if the logical analysis is pushed sufficiently far, an individual. The relation S gives rise to several partial relations and partial domains. We are not going to investigate them here, as they are not relevant to our theory. We shall note, however, that the relation S allows some elegant definitions of some important semantic terms. Let $D_n'R$ be the class of all x_n such that there is at least one x_1, one $x_2 \ldots x_{n-1}$, one x_{n+1}, one $x_{n+2} \ldots x_m$ (m being the number of terms of R) such that $R(x_1, x_2, \ldots, x_n, \ldots, x_m)$. We shall call $D_n'R$ 'the n-th domain of R'. We put now:

2.1. $nom =_{Df.} D_1'S =_{Df.} \hat{a} \{(\exists\, l, f, x)\, S\,(a, l, f, x)\}$

2.2. $lin =_{Df.} D_2'S =_{Df.} \hat{l} \{(\exists\, a, f, x)\, S\,(a, l, f, x)\}$

2.3. $rat =_{Df.} D_3'S =_{Df.} \hat{f} \{(\exists\, a, l, x)\, S\,(a, l, f, x)\}$

2.4. $res =_{Df.} D_4'S =_{Df.} \hat{x} \{(\exists\, a, l, f)\, S\,(a, l, f, x)\}$.

The above definitions define the classes of names (*2.1*), languages (*2,2*), contents (*2,3*) and things (*2.4*).

3. *Analogy is always a relation involving two names*

We contend that analogy, as well as univocity and equivocity, is not an absolute property of *one* name, but a relation involving *two* names at least. If this seems contrary to tradition, it is because of the use the classical authors made of the formula 'the same name': they meant two names of the same form, but spoke, for the reason mentioned above (§ 2), of a single name. If, however, our considerations about the names are admitted, we are compelled to say that no single name is, strictly speaking, univocal, equivocal, or analogical. A single name may have a clear meaning or a confused meaning; but it has always *one* meaning only, and it is not possible to speak about identity or diversity of its meanings, which is required, if we have to define univocity, equivocity, or analogy.

4. The sixteen relations between two semantic complexes

Now if our relations involve two meaning names, they must be relations between two semantic complexes; and as the nature of these relations depends on the relations holding between the terms of both complexes, they will be octadic relations, each complex being a tetradic relation. The general form of such relations will be consequently the following:

$$R(a, b, l, m, f, g, x, y) \, ,$$

where a and b are names, l and m languages, f and g contents, x and y things, while we have $S(a, l, f, x)$ and $S(b, m, g, y)$.

The question arises now, how many relevant relations are there of the above type. This depends, evidently, on the number of dyadic relations between the terms a-b, l-m, f-g and x-y. Such dyadic relations are very numerous, indeed, infinite in number; but for each couple two relations only are relevant, namely, $I(a, b)$ and $\sim I(a, b)$ for names; $l = m$ and $l \neq m$ for languages; $f = g$ and $f \neq g$ for contents; $x = y$ and $x \neq y$ for things. Thus there are sixteen and only sixteen relevant relations between two semantic complexes. The following table enumerates them:

No.	a, b	l, m	f, g	x, y	No.	a, b	l, m	f, g	x, y
1.	I	$=$	$=$	$=$	9.	$\sim I$	$=$	$=$	$=$
2.	I	$=$	$=$	$\neq$	10.	$\sim I$	$=$	$=$	$\neq$
3.	I	$=$	$\neq$	$=$	11.	$\sim I$	$=$	$\neq$	$=$
4.	I	$=$	$\neq$	$\neq$	12.	$\sim I$	$=$	$\neq$	$\neq$
5.	I	$\neq$	$=$	$=$	13.	$\sim I$	$\neq$	$=$	$=$
6.	I	$\neq$	$=$	$\neq$	14.	$\sim I$	$\neq$	$=$	$\neq$
7.	I	$\neq$	$\neq$	$=$	15.	$\sim I$	$\neq$	$\neq$	$=$
8.	I	$\neq$	$\neq$	$\neq$	16.	$\sim I$	$\neq$	$\neq$	$\neq$

This table should replace the traditional division of names into univocal, equivocal, and synonymous ones. As we are, however, not interested in the establishment of a full semantic theory, we shall not define all sixteen relations, but only the first four which are directly relevant to the theory of analogy.

5. Definition of univocity and equivocity

These four (octadic) relations, which we shall name 'R_1', 'R_2', 'R_3', and 'R_4', are defined as follows:

5.1.　$R_1(a, b, l, m, f, g, x, y) \cdot$
$\quad = {}_{Df}.S(a, l, f, x) \cdot S(b, m, g, y) \cdot I(a, b) \cdot l = m \cdot f = g \cdot x = y$

5.2.　$R_2(a, b, l, m, f, g, x, y) \cdot$
$\quad = {}_{Df}.S(a, l, f, x) \cdot S(b, m, g, y) \cdot I(a, b) \cdot l = m \cdot f = g \cdot x \neq y$

5.3.　$R_3(a, b, l, m, f, g, x, y) \cdot$
$\quad = {}_{Df}.S(a, l, f, x) \cdot S(b, m, g, y) \cdot I(a, b) \cdot l = m \cdot f \neq g \cdot x = y$

5.4.　$R_4(a, b, l, m, f, g, x, y) \cdot$
$\quad = {}_{Df}.S(a, l, f, x) \cdot S(b, m, g, y) \cdot I(a, b) \cdot l = m \cdot f \neq g \cdot x \neq y$

5.1. is the definition of names which are semantically identical in spite of being (physically) two names. We may call them 'isosemantic' names. 5.2. is the definition of univocal names: *quorum* (x and y) *nomen est commune* [i.e. $I(a, b)$], *ratio autem significata* (f and g) *est simpliciter eadem* ($f = g$). 5.3. is again the definition of names which have the same denotation, but a different connotation; we may term them 'heterologic' from λόγος = *ratio*. Finally 5.4. defines the equivocal names: *quorum* (x and y) *nomen est commune* [i.e. $I(a, b)$], *ratio autem significata simpliciter diversa* ($f = g$). In all cases $l = m$, i.e. both languages are identical. This being so, we may drop '$l = m$' and put 'l' for 'm'. The above definitions of univocity and equivocity will now run as follows:

5.5.　$Un(a, b, l, f, g, x, y) \cdot$
$\quad = {}_{Df}.S(a, l, f, x) \cdot S(b, l, g, y) \cdot I(a, b) \cdot x \neq y \cdot f = g$

5.6.　$Ae(a, b, l, f, g, x, y) \cdot$
$\quad = {}_{Df}.S(a, l, f, x) \cdot S(b, l, g, y) \cdot I(a, b) \cdot x \neq y \cdot f \neq g$

We have used 'Un' to suggest '*univoca*' and 'Ae' to suggest '*aequivoca*'; we also changed, for technical reasons, the order of the two last factors. The following laws, which are immediate consequences of 5.5., will be needed in the latter parts of this paper:

5.7.　$Un(a, b, l, f, g, x, y) \cdot \supset \cdot S(a, l, f, x)$

5.8.　$Un(a, b, l, f, g, x, y) \cdot \supset \cdot S(b, l, f, x) \cdot$

6. *Partial domains and relata*

Each of our relations Un and Ae being heptadic, contains $\binom{7}{6} = 7$ hexadic, $\binom{7}{5} = 21$ pentadic, $\binom{7}{4} = 35$ tetradic, $\binom{7}{3} = 35$ triadic and $\binom{7}{2} = 21$ dyadic partial relations, together 119 (120 with the full relation). We may denote them by 'Un' respectively 'Ae' followed by two figures: one above, indicating the type of the partial relation (e.g. 'Un^5' for a pentadic partial relation of Un), another below, meaning the place which it occupies among partial relations of the given type – the whole between parentheses. E.g. '(Un_2^5)' will mean the second among the pentadic partial relations of Un.

Moreover, each of these partial relations gives rise, exactly as the whole relation does, to many partial domains and relata. The n-th domain of the relation R will be symbolized, as above (§ 2), by '$D_n'R$' and the n-th class of relata of R by '$sg_n'R$'. There are 120 such domains and 120 such classes of relata. We shall not define them all; the scope of the above remarks was only to show how ambiguous the common language is when we use it to speak about univocity or equivocity and, of course, about analogy. We shall, however, use our notation in order to define the traditional terms '*univoca*' and '*aequivoca*'. We need here first a definition of the following partial dyadic relations:

6.1. $(Un_{21}^2) =_{Df.} \hat{x}\hat{y}\{(\exists\, a, b, l, f, g)\, Un\,(a, b, l, f, g, x, y)\}$

6.2. $(Ae_{21}^2) =_{Df.} \hat{x}\hat{y}\{(\exists\, a, b, l, f, g)\, Ae\,(a, b, l, f, g, x, y)\}$.

We can now define the classes called '*univoca*' and '*aequivoca*' which we shall name '*uni*' or '*aeq*':

6.3. $uni =_{Df.} F'(Un_{21}^2)$

6.4. $aeq =_{Df.} F'(Ae_{21}^2)$.

If this would appear too generic, we may use triadic relations, including the language as a term:

6.5. $(Un_{31}^3) =_{Df.} \hat{l}\hat{x}\hat{y}\{(\exists\, a, b, f, g)\, Un\,(a, b, l, f, g, x, y)\}$

6.6. $(Ae_{31}^3) =_{Df.} \hat{l}\hat{x}\hat{y}\{(\exists\, a, b, l, g)\, Ae\,(a, b, l, f, g, x, y)\}$

and consequently:

6.7. $unil =_{Df.} D'_1(Un_{31}^3) \cup D'_2(Un_{31}^3)$

6.8. $aeql =_{Df.} D'_1(Ae_{31}^3) \cup D'_2(Ae_{31}^3)$.

7. *The principles of non-contradiction and excluded middle*

Other important laws of our theory are two formulae which will be called, respectively, 'the law of contradiction' and 'the law of excluded middle for univocal and equivocal names'. We mean by the first that no two names can be univocal and equivocal in respect to the same language, couples of contents and of things. By the second we mean that if such names are not univocal, they must be equivocal, and conversely. It should be clearly understood that this is true only in respect of some determined contents meant by the names, moreover that these names must be of the same form and the things they mean must be non-identical. For nothing prevents two names from being univocal in respect of $f - g$ and, at the same time, equivocal in respect of $h - j$, if $f \neq h$ or $g \neq j$; also, if the names do not mean the contents involved, they are neither univocal nor equivocal in respect of them. The last two conditions follow from our table in § 4.

Consequently, we state our principles in the following form:

7.1. $(a, b, l, f, g, x, y): S(a, l, f, x) \cdot S(b, l, g, y,) \cdot I(a, b) \cdot x \neq y \cdot \supset$
    $\supset \cdot \sim [Un(a, b, l, f, g, x, y) \cdot Ae(a, b, l, f, g, x, y)]$

7.2. $(a, b, l, f, g, x, y): S(a, l, f, x) \cdot S(b, l, g, y) \cdot I(a, b) \cdot x \neq y \cdot \supset$
    $\supset \cdot Un(a, b, l, f, g, x, y) \vee Ae(a, b, l, f, g, x, y) \, .$

Proofs[1]:

(1)	$p \supset \sim (pq \cdot p \sim q)$	(axiom)
(2)	$p \supset \cdot pq \vee p \sim q$	(axiom)
(3)	$\sim (f = g) \cdot = _{Df.} \cdot f \neq g$	(definition)
(4)	$S(a, l, f, x) \cdot S(b, l, g, y) \cdot I(a, b) \cdot x \neq y : \supset$	

    $\supset : \sim [S(a, l, f, x) \cdot S(b, l, g, y) \cdot I(a, b) \cdot x \neq y \cdot f = g] :$
    $: S(a, l, f, x) \cdot S(b, l, g, y) \cdot I(a, b) \cdot x \neq y \cdot \sim (f = g) :$

by (1) putting $\dfrac{S(a, l, f, x) \cdot S(b, l, g, y) \cdot I(a, b) \cdot x \neq y}{p}, \dfrac{f = g}{q}$

(5) $= 7.1$

by (4), (3), 5.5 and 5.6 with the rule for adjunction of quantifiers.

(6) $S(a, l, f, x) \cdot S(b, l, g, y) \cdot I(a, b) \cdot x \neq y : \supset$
    $\supset : S(a, l, f, x) \cdot S(b, l, g, y) \cdot I(a, b) \cdot x \neq y \cdot f = g \cdot \vee$
    $\vee \cdot S(a, l, f, x) \cdot S(b, l, g, y) \cdot I(a, b) \cdot x \neq y \cdot \sim (f = g)$

by (2) with the same substitutions as for (4)

(7) $= 7.2$

by (6), (3), 5.5 and 5.6 with the rule for adjunction of quantifiers.

---

[1] The method used is that of the *Principia Mathematica;* therefore what we call a 'proof' is rather a sketch of a proof. Rigorous proof could be, however, easily built along the lines given here. (This applies to all proofs contained in the present paper.)

The law of excluded middle shows that the classical Thomists were right when they named their *analoga 'aequivoca a consilio'*, considering them as a subclass of the class of *aequivoca,* and that some modern Thomists are wrong when they put analogy as a third class coordinated to univocity and equivocity. Incidentally it may be remarked that the authors of the *Principia Mathematica* used an exact translation of the ,*aequivocatio a consilio'* when they coined the expression 'systematic ambiguity'. As a matter of fact, they were treating of analogy.

8. On the generic notions of analogy

Analogy will be, according to the above analyses, a heptadic relation between two names, a language, two contents and two things (at least). The names will be of the same form; the things must be different. How the contents are related we must still investigate. If we suppose that the answer to that question is expressed by 'F', the generic definition of analogy will be the following:

8.1. $An(a, b, l, f, g, x, y) \cdot =$
$$= _{Df.} \cdot S(a, l, f, x) \cdot S(b, l, g, y) \cdot I(a, b) \cdot x \neq y \cdot F .$$

Moreover, using *7.2* we may say that analogy is either a kind of univocity or a kind of equivocity. According to tradition it is certainly not the first. Thus it must be the second. We may put therefore:

8.2. $An(a, b, l, f, g, x, y) \cdot = _{Df.} \cdot Ae(a, b, l, f, g, x, y) \cdot F .$

The question arises now, if there is a factor G such that F would be identical with the product of G with another factor, say H_n, G being identical in all kinds of analogy, H_n different for each; the definitions of the successive kinds of analogy would be constructed by putting in *8.2* for 'F' first '$G \cdot H_1$', then '$G \cdot H_2$' and so on. If it be so, we could say that the name 'analogy' is univocal; if not, i.e. if there could be no common factor G, it would be equivocal.

As a matter of fact some well known Thomists asserted that the name 'analogy' is an analogical name, i.e. (according to *8.2*) an equivocal one. We are not going to discuss this assertion, but limit ourselves to a correct formulation of it. This requires, however, some preliminary steps.

9. Expansion of the theory to higher levels

We must first note, that we are already dealing with a situation that is far more complex than that which is met in classical formal logic. As a matter of fact, all artificial symbols of any system of contemporary formal logic belong to the same semantic level, namely to the object language, i.e. each of them means some object, but none of them means a symbol of an object. But in the theory developed above we are using symbols belonging to a higher level, namely our symbols 'a' and 'b', which are names of names, i.e. symbols of symbols.

In order to supply the last sentence with a more definite meaning, let us introduce the following recursive definition: (1) the object language is the first level; (2) a language such that at least one term of it is a symbol of a symbol belonging to the n-th level, but none is a symbol of such term, is the $n + 1$ level; (3) a relation holding between objects of which at least one is of the n-th level, and none is of the $n + 1$ level, is of the n-th level.

It will appear that our a, b and also S, Un, Ae etc. are of the second level; consequently the *names* of these will belong to the third level. Now when we say that 'analogy' is an analogical name, the word 'analogy' is a *name* of An; thus it belongs to the third level. We have to investigate if and how we are allowed to extend our theory to that level, for everything we said until now was clearly situated on the second level.

Let us note first that the laws of the third level would be, as far as structure is concerned, exactly similar to these met on the second. For if we say that 'analogy' is analogical, we mean that two names, say A and B mean in our new language (which is, by the way, the third level), the relations An_1 and An_2 of the objects ($a_1, b_1, l_1, f_1, g_1, x_1, y_1$) and ($a_2, b_2, l_2, f_2, g_2, x_2, y_2$). The last two may be considered as classes; but there is nothing to prevent us from considering them as objects, as the relations An_1 and An_2 are true contents of them. Let us put 'X' for the first and 'Y' for the second. We shall obtain the following exact formulation of the thesis 'analogy is analogical':

$$AN(A, B, L, An_1, An_2, X, Y).$$

Here all symbols (except the parentheses and commas) are different from those used in the former paragraphs; and yet the structure is not only similar, but strictly identical with the structure of

$$An(a, b, l, f, g, x, y).$$

It is also clear that the whole of our previous analyses might have been repeated on the third level. We would reach a theory, whose terms and meanings would be different from the theory we developed above, but whose structure would be completely identical.

This suggests an important remark. Analyses of such kind involve the use of the idea of structural identity, or isomorphism. Now, according the to theory we shall propose, this means analogy of proportionality. It seems, consequently, that we cannot treat adequately the problem of the generic notion of analogy without a previous examination of analogy of proportionality.

10. Analogy of one-one attribution

Among the several kinds of analogy there are only two that are really relevant: analogy of attribution and analogy of proportionality. Two names which are related by the first will be called 'attributively analogous'; similarly, two names related by the latter will be called 'proportionally analogous'.

We are starting with the first kind. Here again there is one relation called 'analogia unius ad alterum' – in our terminology 'one-one analogy' (symbolically 'At') – and another called 'analogia plurium ad unum', here 'many-one analogy' (symbolically 'Atm'). Let us begin with the first, which is the more fundamental.

We have two things, x and y and two contents, f and g; the names a and b are equivocal in regard to them, but there is still another characteristic: x is the cause of y or y the cause of x. Writing '$C(x, y)$' for 'x is the cause of y' we shall have:

10.1. $At(a, b, l, f, g, x, y) \cdot$
$$= {}_{Df.} \cdot Ae(a, b, l, f, g, x, y) \cdot C(x, y) \vee C(y, x) .$$

This is, however, rather unsatisfactory, for the connection of f and g is not shown, the relation of causality not being analyzed. We cannot, of course, give a complete analysis of this highly complex notion here. We shall note only that the relation of causality is a pentadic relation which holds between two things, two contents and a peculiar dyadic relation between the things; e.g. the food is the cause of the health of the animal, if and only if there is a content f (health) present in the food (x) such that, if a peculiar relation R (here: of being eaten) is established between x and the animal (y), another content g (the health of the animal) appears in y. Writing '$C(f, x, R, g, y)$' for this relation we shall have:

10.2. $At(a, b, l, f, g, x, y) \cdot$
  $= _{Df.} \cdot Ae(a, b, l, f, g, x, y) \cdot (\exists R) \cdot C(f, x, R, g, y) \text{ v}$
  $\text{v } C(g, y, R, f, x) .$

The alternative is necessary, according to the traditional doctrine, as there may be an analogy independent of the direction of causality.

11. Analogy of many-one attribution

The second kind of analogy of attribution is clearly derived from the first. The many-one analogy holds, namely, between two names a and b, if and only if there is a third name c, such that both a and b are attributively analogous (according to 10.2) with c:

11.1. $Atm(a, b, l, f, g, x, y) \cdot$
  $= _{Df.} \cdot (\exists c, h, z) \cdot At(a, c, l, f, h, x, z) \cdot$
  $\cdot At(b, c, l, g, h, y, z) .$

Let x be food, y urine, z animal, f, g, h the contents called 'health' of, respectively, x, y, z, and a, b, c the names of these contents. There will be a many-one analogy of a in respect of b.

We may still distinguish four further subclasses of this class of analogical names, for in 11.1 we may have either

(1) $C(f, x, R, h, z) \cdot C(g, y, R, h, z)$ — or
(2) $C(f, x, R, h, z) \cdot C(h, z, R, g, y)$ — or
(3) $C(h, z, R, f, x) \cdot C(g, y, R, h, z)$ — or
(4) $C(h, z, R, f, x) \cdot C(h, z, R, g, y) .$

12. Conditions of analogy of proportionality

There are, according to tradition, two conditions for this kind of analogy: the contents must be non-identical, i.e. we must have equivocity; still, the syllogism having as middle terms a couple of proportionally analogous names must be a correct formula. This is secured, according to classical writers, by the fact that these middle terms mean something 'proportionally common' in both cases, or that there is an *analogatum commune* containing *in confuso* the contents meant by both names.

It seems at first, that these requirements are contradictory: for, if the meanings of the two names are quite different, one can hardly see how a syllogism with them as middle terms may be a correct formula. As a matter of fact, not only is there a logical theory capable of fulfilling both requirements without contradiction, but it seems even that there are *two* such theories. It seems, namely, that one theory is suggested by the '*proportionaliter commune*', the other by the '*confuse*'. We shall call the former 'isomorphic', the latter 'alternative theory'. As far as is known to the writer, St. Thomas used the isomorphic theory, while the alternative seems to be originated by Cajetan.

13. The alternative theory

The central idea of the alternative theory may be explained as follows: we have to do with three names; one of them means the content f, the other the content g, f and g being the *analogata particularia*; the third name means the *analogatum commune,* namely, the alternative of f and g, symbolically $f \cup g$. We shall give to that expression a sufficiently clear meaning by putting

13.1. $[f \cup g] x \cdot = _{Df.} \cdot fx \vee gx$.

A rather complex situation arises here because of admission of three names: this makes an expansion of our previous formulae to three complexes necessary, and the basic formula for analogy of proportionality becomes a relation of ten terms. Once a definition of this form is established, the (heptadic) relations analogous to *Un* and *Ae* will appear as partial relations of the general one, and the verbal formulae as elliptic. We shall not, however, define this general relation in that way, as, for several reasons, to be explained later (§ 16), the whole alternative theory appears as inadequate. But we are going to investigate the validity of a syllogism *in Barbara* with proportionally analogous middle terms. For the use in that inquiry we define the analogy of proportionality (*Anp*) according to the alternative theory as a heptadic relation in the following way:

13.2.   *Anp* $(a, b, l, f, g, x, y) \cdot$
    $= _{Df.} \cdot Ae(a, b, l, f, g, x, y) \cdot (\exists h) \cdot f = [g \cup h]$.

This is a partial relation contained in the full relation of analogy described above.

14. On formal validity of syllogism

If we wish to investigate the validity of a syllogism with analogical middle terms we meet a serious difficulty unknown in current formal

108

logic. For in current formal logic it is always supposed that a formula which is verbally valid is also formally valid; the reason of this supposition is that all terms used in current formal logic are univocal symbols. Here, however, the situation is different, as we have to deal with analogical names. We need, consequently, a distinction between the verbal and formal validity of a formula; moreover we need to know when a verbally valid formula is also formally valid. This is by no means a universal rule, as the case of the syllogism with equivocal and non-analogical middle terms shows. We are not going to investigate the problem in its full generality, but we will limit ourselves to a single case, the syllogism in *Barbara*.

We shall first construct two languages:

(1) A first-level univocal language. This will be the language of the theory of classes, interpreted as a logic of contents. In it the mode *Barbara* will run as follows:

$$f \subset g \cdot h \subset f \cdot \supset \cdot h \subset g \, .$$

(2) A second-level analogical language. This will contain all symbols used until now (small Latin letters being sometimes substituted by small Greek letters and indexes being added to them), with addition of the following: (i) 'Π'; a formula composed of 'Π' followed by 'a', followed by 'b' will be interpreted as meaning the formula '$a \subset b$'; (ii) '$+$'; a formula such as '$\Pi + a + b$' will be read: 'a formula composed of Π followed by a, followed by b'; (iii) '$\varepsilon\, T$'; '$F\,\varepsilon\, T$' will be read: 'F is a true theorem'.

The proofs will be developed in a second-level language, containing as subclasses the above two. We shall proceed as follows. Given the (second-level) premises A and B such that $A\,\varepsilon\, T \cdot B\,\varepsilon\, T$, we wish to prove that the (verbally correct) conclusion C (of the same level) is a true theorem, i.e. that $C\,\varepsilon\, T$. We translate A and B into the first-level language, apply to the result the laws of classical formal logic and obtain a conclusion, which we re-translate into the second level language; if we are able to obtain $C\,\varepsilon\, T$ in that way, the formula 'if $A\,\varepsilon\, T \cdot B\,\varepsilon\, T$, then $C\,\varepsilon\, T$' is clearly a valid formula and the formal validity of the mode, whose premises are A and B, and the conclusion C, is proved.

We put as a law of translation the intuitively evident:

14.1. $S(a, l, f, x) \cdot S(b, l, g, y) : \supset : \Pi + a + b \, \varepsilon\, T \cdot \equiv \cdot f \subset g \, .$

With the help of *14.1* we can easily prove that a syllogism in *Barbara* with univocal middle terms is a formally valid formula; but we cannot prove it if the middle terms are either purely equivocal or attributively analogical. Alongside of *14.1* we shall need still another law of translation for cases where an existential quantifier is involved:

14.2. $(\exists h) \cdot S(a, l, [f \cup h], x) \cdot S(b, l, g, y) : \supset$

$\qquad \supset : (\exists h) \cdot [f \cup h] \subset g$.

This seems to be also intuitively evident.

15. *The validity of the syllogism in Barbara with analogical middle terms according to the alternative theory*

In such a syllogism the middle term of the major premise is analogical with regard to the middle term in the minor premise, the situation being this, that the former means alternatively the content meant by the latter *and* some other content. This syllogism, if in *Barbara,* is a valid formula. The proof is rather cumbersome, because of the existential quantifier; we shall however give here a developed sketch of it.

In the first place we need two theorems analogous to *5.7* and *5.8* .These may be proved as follows.

(*1*) $\quad Anp(a, b, l, f, g, x, y) \cdot$

$\qquad \equiv \cdot Ae(a, b, l, f, g, x, y) \cdot (\exists h) \cdot f = [g \cup h]$

$\qquad\qquad$ [by *13.2*]

(*2*) $\quad \equiv \cdot S(a, l, f, x) \cdot S(b, l, g, y) \cdot I(a, b) \cdot x \neq y \cdot$

$\qquad \cdot f \neq g \cdot (\exists h) \cdot f = [g \cup h]$

$\qquad\qquad$ [by (*1*) and *5.6*]

(*3*) $\quad \equiv \cdot (\exists h) \cdot S(a, l, f, x) \cdot S(b, l, g, y) \cdot I(a, b) \cdot$

$\qquad \cdot x \neq y \cdot f \neq g \cdot f = [g \cup h]$

$\qquad\qquad$ [by (*2*) and **10.24* *Principia Mathematica.*]

(*4*) $\quad \equiv \cdot (\exists h) \cdot S(a, l, [g \cup h], x) \cdot S(b, l, g, y) \cdot I(a, b) \cdot$

$\qquad \cdot x \neq y \cdot f \neq g$

$\qquad\qquad$ [by (*3*) and **13.12* *Principia Mathematica.*]

(*5*) $\quad \equiv \cdot (\exists h) \, S(a, l, [g \cup h], x) \cdot (\exists h) \, S(b, l, g, y) \cdot$

$\qquad \cdot (\exists h) \cdot x \neq y \cdot f \neq g$

$\qquad\qquad$ [by (*4*) and **10.5* *Principia Mathematica.*]

15.1. $\quad Anp(a, b, l, f, g, x, y) \cdot \supset \cdot (\exists h) \, S(a, l, [g \cup h], x)$

$\qquad\qquad$ [by (*5*) and '$p \equiv qr \cdot \supset \cdot p \supset q$']

15.2. $Anp(a, b, l, f, g, x, y) \cdot \supset \cdot S(b, l, g, y)$

[by *(5)* and '$p \equiv qrs \cdot \supset \cdot p \supset r$', dropping the quantifier].

We enumerate now the five hypotheses of the syllogism in *Barbara* with analogical middle terms, explained according to the alternative theory:

H1. $\Pi + m_1 + a_1 \, \varepsilon \, T$

H2. $\Pi + b_1 + m_2 \, \varepsilon \, T$

H3. $Anp(m_1, m_2, l, \mu_{,1} \, \mu_2, x, y)$

H4. $Un(a_1, a_2, l, \alpha_1, \alpha_2, z, t)$

H5. $Un(b_1, b_2, l, \beta_1, \beta_2, u, v)$.

The proof of '$\Pi + b_2 + a_2 \, \varepsilon \, T$' runs as follows:

(1)	$(\exists \, h) \, S(m_1, l, [\mu_2 \cup h], x)$	by *H3* and *15.1*
(2)	$S(a_1, l, \alpha_1, z)$	by *H4* and *5.7*
(3)	$(\exists \, h) \cdot [\mu_2 \cup h] \subset \alpha_1$	by *(1)*, *(2)*, *H1* and *14.2*
(4)	$S(b_1, l, \beta_1, u)$	by *H5* and *5.7*
(5)	$S(m_2, l, \mu_2, y)$	by *H3* and *15.2*
(6)	$\beta_1 \subset \mu_2$	by *(4)*, *(5)*, *H2* and *14.1*
(7)	$\beta_1 \subset \mu_2 \cdot (\exists \, h) \cdot [\mu_2 \cup h] \subset \alpha_1$	by *(6)* and *(3)*
(8)	$(\exists \, h) \cdot \beta_1 \subset \mu_2 \cdot [\mu_2 \cup h] \subset \alpha_1$	by *(7)* and **10.35 PM*
(9)	$(\exists \, h) \cdot \beta_1 \subset \alpha_1$	by *(8)*, '$f \subset g \cdot [g \cup h] \subset j \cdot \supset \cdot f \subset j$' and **10.28 PM*
(10)	$\beta_1 \subset \alpha_1$	by *(9)*
(11)	$S(b_2, l, \beta_1, u)$	by *H5* and *5.8*
(12)	$S(a_2, l, \alpha_1, z)$	by *H4* and *5.8*
(13)	$\Pi + b_1 + a_2 \, \varepsilon \, T \cdot \equiv \cdot \beta_1 \subset \alpha_1$	by *(11)*, *(12)* and *14.1*
(14)	$\Pi + b_2 + a_2 \, \varepsilon \, T$	by *(10)* and *(13)*
	Q.E.D.	

16. Criticism of the alternative theory

It has been shown that a syllogism in *Barbara* with analogical middle terms, defined according to the alternative theory, is a formally valid formula. This is, however, the only advantage of this theory. Not even all requirements of theology and metaphysics in regard to the syllogism can be met by means of it. For a syllogism of these sciences has not only analogical middle terms, but also analogical major terms; e.g. when we write 'if every being is good, and God is a being, then God is good,' not only 'being', but also 'good' must be analogical. But this means, according to the alternative theory that *H4* in § 15 should be replaced by

$$Anp(a_1, a_2, l, \alpha_1, \alpha_2, z, t) \, .$$

If so, instead of (3) we would obtain only

$$(\exists\, h) \cdot [\mu_2 \cup h] \subset [\alpha_2 \cup g]$$

which does not allow us to draw the conclusion (*14*). Neither can we try to invert the order of '*f*' and '*g*' in *15.1*; in that case the syllogism would become valid, but the major term in the conclusion would have an alternative meaning, which can hardly be admitted.

Moreover, the theory has other inconveniences. First, the very definition of analogy, as sketched in § 13, is highly unsatisfactory. By saying that two names are analogical if and only if there is a third name meaning alternatively the contents meant by both, we do not show any intrinsic connection between the contents involved; and every couple of names would be analogical, according to that definition, for we can always introduce into our system a new name, meaning, according to definition, precisely the said alternative. Secondly, there are serious gnoseological difficulties. The situation with which we have to deal, is the following: two names are given, and while we know the meaning of the first by direct experience, we do not know in that way the meaning of the second. In order to be able to use that second name correctly, we must supply it with a meaning correlated in some way with the meaning of the first. Now the alternative theory allows nothing of the sort: it only says how we can deal with middle terms having alternative meanings, when both meanings are already known.

These remarks do not lead to the complete rejection of the alternative theory; but they seem to show that it is at least incomplete and should be completed by another theory. The present author believes that this was the position of Cajetan.

17. The isomorphic theory

This theory is based on the following considerations: the *proportionaliter eadem* suggests that there is an identity, not between the contents meant by both analogical terms, but between some relations holding between the first (f) and its thing (x) on one side, the second (g) and its thing (y) on the other. The texts of St. Thomas Aquinas are clear enough here. The said relations are, however, not identical; this is also a traditional thesis, strongly emphasized by all classical Thomists. We may therefore admit, as a first approximation, that, while being non-identical, they are both contained in the same relation. The definition of analogy of proportionality would run, in that case, as follows:

17.1. $Anp(a, b, l, f, g, x, y) \cdot = {}_{Df.} \cdot Ae(a, b, l, f, g, x, y) \cdot$
$(\exists P, Q, R) \cdot fPx \cdot gQy \cdot P \neq Q \cdot P \subseteq R \cdot Q \subseteq R .$

This is, however, not satisfactory. For if 17.1 would be the definition of analogy of proportionality, there would be a material univocal element; analogy would allow us to transfer to the other name some material relations found in the meaning of the first. Now St. Thomas Aquinas and tradition are quite clear as to the negation of such univocity. But 17.1 can be corrected by the affirmation that the common element in both relations is formal, i.e. consists in the isomorphy of these relations. The definition becomes:

17.2. $An(a, b, l, f, g, x, y) \cdot = {}_{Df.} \cdot Ae(a, b, l, f, g, x, y) \cdot$
$\cdot (\exists P, Q) \cdot fPx \cdot gQy \cdot PsmorQ .$

This is what we mean by 'isomorphic theory'. [1] It is strongly supported by the fact that St. Thomas Aquinas uses for illustration of his doctrine mathematical proportionality, the only mathematical function he possessed and a function which makes one immediately think of isomorphy.

One may think, perhaps, that if this be analogy of proportionality, the meaning of our sentences about spirit, God etc., would be extremely poor, indeed limited to some very few formal relations enumerated in the *Principia Mathematica*. But this is not so. It is true that we cannot, as yet, give exact formulations of many formal properties involved in relations used by metaphysics and theology; the reason, however, is not the lack of such formal properties, but the very undeveloped state of biology and of other sciences, from which the metaphysician and the theologian must draw his analogical names (and contents). An immense progress in speculative sciences would arise out of a formalization of these disciplines. And yet, even in the actual state of knowledge, where only

---

[1] This definition is under the danger of trivialization; a better definition would be one by which the quoted relations P and Q are contained in the meaning of a respectively b in l (this proposal was made by P. Lorenzen).

113

mathematics, i.e. the poorest of all sciences, is formalized, we can show, e.g., the difference between the principle and the father by purely formal means – as, evidently, the first is transitive, the second intransitive.

18. The existential interpretation of the mode Barbara

If the isomorphic theory is admitted, a peculiar interpretation must be given to the mode *Barbara* with analogical middle terms. Let us consider the following substitution: 'if all being is good, and God is a being, then God is good.' According to the isomorphic theory the only common element meant by the two 'being' and the two 'good' is a product of some formal relations, say P in the first case and Q in the second. But if it is so, the major must be interpreted as follows: 'for all x: if there is an f such that fPx, then there is a g such that gQy'; the minor will be interpreted in the same manner by the formula 'for all x: if there is an h such that hRx, then there is an f such that fPx'. From this we draw the conclusion 'for all x: if there is an h such that hRx, then there is a g such that gQx.' This would mean: 'if there is an x such that h is the Divinity of x, then there is a g such that g is the Goodness of x.' The law used here is:

18.1. $(x) \cdot (\exists f) fPx \supset (\exists g) gQx : (x) \cdot (\exists h) hRx \supset (\exists f) fPx :$
          $\supset : (x) \cdot (\exists h) hRx \supset (\exists g) gQx .$

This is a correct formula of the logic of predicates.

The remarkable result of the existential interpretation is that the Thomistic idea of analogy becomes sharply formulated in a very anti-univocal sense. For, we do not know, as a result of our reasoning according to *18.1*, anything except that there is something (undetermined as to the content) which has to God the set of quite formal relations Q. And yet, the talk about God's goodness is clearly meaningful; moreover rigorous demonstrations concerning it are possible.

19. The validity of the syllogism with analogical middle terms according to the isomorphic theory

We are going to show now how, in such theory, a syllogism in *Barbara* is a formally valid formula. We meet here, however, two formal difficulties.

First we note that isomorphy, being a relation between two relations, cannot be, as such, treated as a relation in which these relations are contained; now this seems to be necessary if we wish to construct a correct syllogism with analogical middle terms, interpreted according to the isomorphic theory.

This difficulty may be, however, obviated in the following manner. Isomorphy implies the identity of a series of formal properties of the relations involved. These formal properties are different in each case of couples of isomorphic relations; but for each of them *in concreto* a product of such properties may be determined. E.g., in some cases both relations will be included in diversity and will be transitive; in other cases they will be intransitive and asymmetric etc. Now each of these properties may be conceived as a relation in which the given isomorphic relations are contained. This can be done by introducing into the system the name of a new relation, which is treated as a primitive term, but whose meaning is determined by an axiom. E.g. for symmetry we will put a relation S and determine the meaning of 'S' by the axiom $(x, y): xSy \cdot \equiv \cdot xSy \equiv x\check{S}y$. The product of such relations would constitute the relation in which both isomorphic relations are contained.[1]

The other difficulty is strictly operational. It will appear that we shall need an expansion of our *17.2* in order that the name of the common relation R, in which the relations P and Q are contained, might be treated as an argument of '*Anp*'. If so, a new relation must be defined, namely an octadic relation containing as terms, besides the seven stated in *17.2*, also R. We shall define it as follows:

19.1. $Anp(a, b, l, f, g, x, y, R) \cdot = {}_{Df.} \cdot Ae(a, b, l, f, g, x, y) \cdot$
$\cdot (\exists P, Q, R) \cdot fPx \cdot gQy \cdot P \neq Q \cdot P \neq R \cdot Q \neq R \cdot$
$\cdot P \subseteq R \cdot Q \subseteq R \cdot R \varepsilon \, Form \,.$

By '*Form*' we mean the class of all formal relations, as described in § 17. There will be three laws of translation, analogous to *14.1*:

19.2. $Anp(m_1, m_2, l, \mu_1, \mu_2, x, y, P) \cdot Anp(a_1, a_2, l, \alpha_1, \alpha_2, z, t, Q): \supset$
$\supset : \Pi + m_1 + a_1 \varepsilon \, T \cdot \equiv \cdot (x) \cdot (\exists f) fPx \supset (\exists g) gQx \,.$

19.3. $Anp(b_1, b_2, l, \beta_1, \beta_2, u, v, R) \cdot Anp(m_1, m_2, l, \mu_1, \mu_2, x, y, P): \supset$
$\supset : \Pi + b_1 + m_2 \varepsilon \, T \cdot \equiv \cdot (x) \cdot (\exists h) hRx \supset (\exists f) fPx \,.$

---

[1] The author is conscious that the proposed solution is highly un-orthodox; he would be glad to find anything better. It must be remembered, however, that the whole difficulty is purely operational; it seems intuitively evident that once there is a common property, the syllogism is valid.

19.4. $Anp(b_1, b_2, l, \beta_1, \beta_2, u, v, R) \cdot Anp(a_1, a_2, l, \alpha_1, \alpha_2, z, t, Q) : \supset$

$\supset : \Pi + b_2 + a_2 \, \varepsilon \, T \cdot \equiv \cdot (x) \cdot (\exists \, h) \, hRx \supset (\exists \, g) \, gQx$.

Our hypotheses are

H1. $\quad \Pi + m_1 + a_1 \, \varepsilon \, T$

H2. $\quad \Pi + b_1 + m_2 \, \varepsilon \, T$

H3. $\quad Anp(m_1, m_2, l, \mu_1, \mu_2, x, y, P)$

H4. $\quad Anp(a_1, a_2, l, \alpha_1, \alpha_2, z, t, Q)$

H5. $\quad Anp(b_1, b_2, l, \beta_1, \beta_2, u, v, R)$.

The proof of '$\Pi + b_2 + a_2 \, \varepsilon \, T$' runs as follows:

(1)	$(x) \cdot (\exists f) f Px \supset (\exists g) gQx$	by *H3, H4, H1* and *19.2*
(2)	$(x) \cdot (\exists \, h) hRx \supset (\exists f) f Px$	by *H5, H3, H2* and *19.3*
(3)	$(x) \cdot (\exists \, h) hRx \supset (\exists g) gQx$	by *(1), (2)* and *18.1*
(4)	$\Pi + b_2 + a_2 \, \varepsilon \, T \cdot \equiv \cdot (x) (\exists \, h) hRx \supset (\exists g) gQx$	
		by *H5, H4* and *19.4*
(5)	$\Pi + b_2 + a_2 \, \varepsilon \, T$	by *(4)* and *(3)*

Q.E.D.

20. *On analogy in recent logic*

While the classical Thomists used analogy in ontology and theology, but not in logic, recent writers seem to make a constant use of it in formal logic. We noticed already that the authors of the *Principia Mathematica* re-invented the very name used for analogy by the Thomists (§ 7) and that analogy appears in the construction of semantics (§ 9). The last phenomenon is connected with the theory of types. It is known that, in order to avoid contradictions, we are bound to divide all objects treated by logic (or all logical expressions) into classes called 'types'. The formulae used in each type have quite a different meaning, but exactly the same structure as the formulae used in another. This means that the formal properties involved are identical i.e. that we have to do with analogy, at least if the isomorphic theory is accepted.

The question arises as to why analogy has penetrated the domain of formal logic. The answer seems to be given by the theory of Prof. H. Scholz, who says that recent formal logic is nothing else than a part of classic ontology.[1] As a matter of fact, recent formal logic generally deals, not with rules, but with laws of the being in its whole generality;

---

[1] H. Scholz, *Metaphysik als strenge Wissenschaft*, Köln 1941.

most of the laws contained in the *Principia Mathematica,* e.g., as opposed to metalogical rules, are such laws. If this is so, it is not to be wondered at that some consideration must have been given to analogy, for 'being' is an analogical term and so are the names of all properties, relations, etc., belonging to being as such.

One curious feature of these developments is that the highly trained mathematical logicians who had to speak about analogy, spoke about it in a very loose and inexact way. What, for example, the *Principia Mathematica* contains on the subject is far more rudimentary than the classic Thomistic doctrine. Yet, recent formal logic, once applied to the language itself, supplies superior tools for the elaboration of that notion. The present paper is believed to contain only a very small sub-class of the class of theorems on analogy, which may and should be elaborated by means of recent formal logic.

IX

I. M. BOCHENSKI

THE PROBLEM OF UNIVERSALS *

The present paper contains an attempt to restate *some* aspects of the problem of universals (abridged here as 'PU') in the frame of recent logical semiotical techniques, and in face of some new ontological doctrines. A *solution* of the PU will not be attempted here. The method is purely *speculative,* and no references will be made to history, except to some quite recent ideas.[1] The language used will be *informal,* as it is necessary in a study of this kind, preceding the stage of formalization.

Every statement of the PU is relative to a frame of reference, essentially ontological. It is necessary therefore to state the main point of the frame assumed here first. This may be termed 'ontological individualism'. The author takes the position that every extra-mental thing in the universe is singular, not universal. Thinkers who proceed from other ontological views may find that the problematic presented here is irrelevant; thus one who believes that the real world contains classes and classes of classes and so on, actual or possible, will find no problems at all of this sort in this paper. But those problems are very real to an individualist – and they are stated here from *his* point of view.

1. The five levels

We may state provisionally the PU in the following form: 'Are there universals?' Then the first task would be to determine what we mean by 'universals'. It appears, however, that the question is ambiguous: the term has been and is still used in regard to different levels or realms of

---

* From: I. M. Bocheński, Alonso Church, Nelson Goodman, *The Problem of Universals A Symposium*. Notre Dame, Indiana, (1956) 33–57.
[1] The terminology of this paper is that of contemporary American philosophy. The author is indebted for many ideas formulated in the present paper to several logicians with whom he had the privilege to discuss the PU. As far as the literature of the subject is concerned, the indebtedness to W. V. O. Quine (*From a Logical Point of View,* Cambridge, Mass., 1953) will be obvious to the reader in spite of the disagreement in fundamental points.

reality and it seems to have a different meaning in each of them. At least five such levels have been quoted, namely that of linguistic symbols, of subjective mental entities, of objective meanings, of phenomenal realities and of transcendent entities. Our first task is, therefore, to describe them briefly.

(1) *Linguistic symbols,* words and others. Those symbols are *bodies,* namely heaps of dry ink on paper, of chalk on blackboards, etc. They may also be events, namely bundles of waves in the air; but in order to simplify, we shall be concerned only with written symbols, i.e. with inscriptions.

(2) *Subjective mental entities.* When we know things, we form in our mind certain images, concepts, etc. It must be stressed that those subjective entities are *real,* consequently individual, being parts of an individual mind.

(3) *Objective meanings.* By that we mean exactly what the old Stoics termed λεκτά, namely 'what is said'. They were used to say that the λεκτόν is – in opposition to words – what a Greek, but not a Barbarian understands. The λεκτά or objective meanings do not exist otherwise than *as* meanings either of linguistic symbols or/and subjective mental entities. They are therefore *toto genere* different from the transcendent entities (5), which are sometimes said to exist independently of any subject. Yet they are also different from subjective mental entities. This can be seen in the following way: when two men discuss, say a false mathematical theorem, they have distinct subjective concepts of it, and yet they talk about *the same,* i.e. they are concerned with the same objective meaning.

(4) *Phenomenal realities.* The word 'phenomenal' is used here in the Husserlian and *not* in the phenomenalist or Kantian way; we mean by it simply what is given, either to sensual, or (through it) to intellectual direct apprehension.[1] The word 'reality' is taken in its everyday meaning, as opposed to the so-called 'ideal' entities of the Platonists.

(5) *Transcendent entities.* Those entities are supposed to exist in some way different from real beings, 'beyond' reality. One classical instance is the Platonic Idea.

Out of those five levels we may immediately discard two, namely the second and the fifth. We may discard the level of subjective mental entities (2), as those are real, concrete and consequently, play only the role

---

[1] The PU may be also stated for non-phenomenal realities; but it is convenient to limit our attention to the phenomenal entities. We also believe that, in history, those entities were considered first of all.

of *symbols:* but that function can be far better examined by studying linguistic symbols. It is true that the subjective mental entities become very important once we enter into epistemological considerations; but we are not concerned here primarily with them.

We also discard the level of transcendent entities (5). There may or may not be such entities. But (a) we are unable to find any trace of direct intellectual vision of such objects in ourselves, while (b) if their existence has to be inferred, inference must presuppose some data involved in the level of phenomenal reality. This does not mean that research about such entities should be considered impossible or fruitless; but we think that we must first examine the other levels and, in particular, the level of phenomenal realities.

The result is, that our provisional statement of the PU 'Are there universals?' must be stated separately for each of our three levels: that of linguistic symbols, that of objective meanings, and that of real entities.

We shall do it, beginning with the level of language.

2. The PU for linguistic symbols

A linguistic symbol is called 'universal', if it is applied to several (at least two) distinct objects. It seems, however, that more commonly we do not apply the *same symbol* to two objects, but rather two symbols having *the same shape* (e.g. graphic shape). Thus we may say that a term is universal if and only if two terms of the same shape as it (one or both of which may be identical with it) are predicated of two distinct objects – where 'predicated' simply means 'used in regard of'. The same may be stated in a more precise way as follows:

2.1 For all x and l: x is universal symbol of l if and only if there is at least one of each y, z, t, and u such that (a) y and z are symbols of l, (b) x, y, and z have the same shape, (c) y is predicated of t and z of u, (d) t is distinct from u.

The above definition can be put into a symbolic form by writing '$Un(x, l)$' for 'x is a universal symbol of l', 'xSl' for 'x is a symbol of l', 'xy' for 'x has the same shape as y', 'xPy' for 'x is predicated of y'. We get then the following formula:

2.2 $(x,l): Un(x,l) \cdot \equiv \cdot (\exists y, z, t, u) \cdot ySl \cdot zSl \cdot yHx \cdot zHx \cdot yPt \cdot zPu \cdot t \neq u$.

That there are such universal terms both in natural and in artificial

120

languages is certain and that is not the question. We may ask, however: (1) are such universal symbols parts of every *working* language? (By 'working' we mean a language in which science and, among others, classical mathematics can be stated); (2) what *sort* of universal symbols must be parts of a working language?

Now the first question can be readily answered: every working language does contain some universal symbols. The reason is that we are bound to classify things and cannot do so without universal symbols.

The second question is a far more complex, but also a more important one. Its relevance can be understood if we consider that the PU for other levels is at least somewhat connected with the universal linguistic symbols; consequently it appears that, if we can dispense with some classes of universal symbols, the PU will not rise for the corresponding meanings and entities. That is why we must dedicate some attention to our question.

3. *On the structure of language*

There are no 'absolutely' primitive *terms* which could not be defined by other terms; we can always devise a system in which terms, primitive in another, will be defined. But we may legitimately ask if there are absolutely primitive *syntactical categories*. By a 'syntactical category' we mean a class of terms such that they can be mutually substituted in a well-formed formula of the given language without the formula ceasing to be well-formed. By 'primitive syntactical category' we mean a syntactical category the elements of which cannot be defined otherwise than by terms belonging to that syntactical category. The question is, if in every working language there must be some primitive syntactical category of universal terms.

In order to examine that problem, we shall limit our attention to one language, namely that of the *Principia*. It is the simplest known working language, simplest as far as the number of primitive syntactical categories is concerned. All other languages which are known to be working languages (as that of Leśniewski) or supposed to be so (as the *New Foundations* of Quine) have practically the same primitive categories – with one exception, namely that sometimes that of class-names is substituted to the category of functors. We may, consequently, limit ourselves to an examination of the language of the *Principia*.

It contains the following five primitive syntactical categories:

(1) individual (variable) names, like 'x'
(2) monadic, name-determining functors, like 'ϕ'
(3) existential quantifiers, like '$(\exists x)$'
(4) sentences, like 'p'
(5) syntactical category of dyadic sentential functors, containing only one class of symbols, of the same shape, namely that of the stroke '$|$' (truth table '0111') or, alternatively, of the Peirce's *amphec* (truth table '0001').

This language can be changed by introducing the syntactical category of class-names (with the epsilon) instead of that of monadic name-determining functors, which then can be dropped; we shall, however, disregard that possibility as this seems to commit us more than the *Principia* do to the existence of classes (which we disbelieve) and obliges us, moreover, to introduce the epsilon, i.e. a new primitive syntactical category.

The language of the *Principia* does contain and, as a matter of fact, *must* contain in order to be a working language, more than the above five categories. It contains e.g. second level functors (functor-determining functors) and quantified functors, i.e. functors' quantifiers or their equivalents. We shall see later on how those additional categories can be made irrelevant to the PU and why some of the above cannot. For the moment we are limiting our attention to our set of five and shall try to determine which among them *may* give rise to the PU.

The category of names (1) obviously does not, as its elements are *individual* names; the category of quantifiers (3) is also irrelevant for our question, as its elements serve exclusively to assert the existence of something and do not give any information about the nature of that something; the sentences (4) can always be replaced by a functor followed by an argument, which will be an individual name. Consequently we are left with (2) and (5) only: the monadic, name-determining functors and the stroke (or the amphec). (5) would be in itself a sufficient reason to worry about the PU. But as the stroke (or amphec) is a *logical* constant, it offers some difficulties of its own, while the aspects of the PU connected with it are the same, as those to which the name-determining functors give rise, we may disregard it here.

All other syntactical categories of the *Principia,* except those of higher types, can be disposed of. In particular, the universal quantifier '(x)' may be defined by the existential quantifier and the negator (which, in turn will be defined by the stroke); the classes can be substituted, in use, by functors qualifying name-variables; the relations may be reduced to classes by the Wiener-Kuratowski method.

4. On the meanings of 'meaning'

We turn now to the PU for the third of our levels, that of objective meanings, or of λεκτά. Contrary to what happened on the first level, we are faced here with *two* distinct problems: (1) are there meanings at all? (2) are there *universal* meanings? A positive answer to (1) is obviously presupposed to the meaningfulness of (2). But this is the most controverted, and, we may add, the most confused question, because of the misunderstandings concerning the very term 'meaning'.

In regard to it, the following distinctions must be made:

(a) The meaning of a term may consist entirely in the set of syntactical rules concerning that term; this is the case in a formalistic language without interpretation. That sort of meaning we shall call *'syntactic'*.

(b) Second, there may be a meaning which is not exhausted by the syntactical rules; this is always the case, when there is an interpretation of the language under consideration. We shall call such meaning, in spite of the redundance of the terms used, *'semantic meaning'*.

A further distinction may be made in the last sort of meaning. According to a widespread (and never clearly stated) view, the semantic meaning consists in the method of verification. This applies directly to sentences for which the statement runs: 'a sentence is semantically meaningful if and only if there is a method of verifying it'; or even stronger; 'the meaning of a sentence *is* its method of verification'. As far as symbols which are not sentences (e.g. functors) are concerned, they are said to be semantically meaningful if and only if a sentence containing them as parts is meaningful in the above sense of the word. Whatever may be thought of that view, it should be clear that a symbol which has *only* that sort of meaning has still a *semantic* meaning, namely, that its meaning is not exhausted by the rules of operation on *symbols,* but consists in some rules of operations on extra-linguistic things. We shall call that meaning 'the *semantic operational meaning*'.

But there may be still another sort of semantic meaning, namely that which is commonly said 'to be meant' by a symbol, that to which the symbol has a semantic correlate apart from the method of verification. This we shall term the '*eidetic meaning*'.

We may now state our view on the question. We allow that some symbols have exclusively a syntactic meaning and that every symbol which is semantically meaningful at all has *also* a semantically operational meaning; but we think that it is preposterous to deny that at least some of our symbols have an eidetic meaning. What the adversaries of that view do, is to invoke machines, which are, supposedly, able to behave exactly as men do in face of an excitation taking the place of symbols; such machines do not produce, obviously, any sort of meanings. About that we shall say only that the proof that this can be done in all cases has never been produced. On the other hand, the givenness of eidetic meanings in our own thought is obvious. We do not deny that *some* symbols can be eidetically meaningless; we even admit that some are semantically meaningless i.e. more than the adversaries admit.

To be short, the situation is the following: (1) our direct view of what is going on in us, when we understand a symbol, commits us to admitting *eidetic* meanings; (2) there is no pragmatic test for the contrary produced by the adversaries. It may be added that (3) the whole theory of verifiability is so desperately confused that we do not see *any* reason for assuming anything so poetical and romantic.

Moreover, we believe that there *are* stronger reasons than those, already, it seems, sufficiently strong ones, against the said theory. But as we are not prepared, as now, to state them in a sufficiently rigorous shape, we shall not state them at all – this the more, as we are above all interested in the level of reality, not in that of meanings.

5. *The PU for objective meanings*

We may consider now our second question: given that there are eidetic meanings, are there *universal* eidetic meanings? This problem may be again subdivided. We may ask, first, what sort of universal linguistic symbols must be assumed as eidetically meaningful, and, second, given that there is a non-empty class of such eidetically meaningful symbols, if its elements must be assumed to be univocal, namely if two symbols of the same shape must have the same meaning.

As far as the first question is concerned, we may always consider a given language as a purely formalistic system without attaching any interpretation, i.e. any semantic meaning to its symbols. This has been proposed for logic and mathematics by Goodman and Quine, who suggest that we may consider them as a pure abacus. Their method permits to dispose at least of the above mentioned meaningful higher-level functors and quantifiers. It seems that such functors and quantifiers occur *only* in formal sciences, and are not needed in empirical sciences. When mathematics is used in them, or at least those parts of mathematics where the said symbols occur, it seems that it may be considered as an abacus. Thus our restriction of the PU for symbols to the five categories enumerated is justified. We can always get rid of other categories, and consequently of other meanings by that method.

But if we try to dispense with monadic, name-determining functors, we fail and we *must* fail. The reason is that a formalized system in order to be a system at all, i.e. to have any use, must have some meta-linguistic operational rules which cannot be deprived of all semantic meaning, as they must be understood to be applied. Now in these rules monadic, name-determining functors recur. We must have, e.g. the *modus ponendo ponens* or some rule similar to it. That rule will be e.g. formulated in the following way: 'given a conditional composed of two sentences, and given a sentence of the same shape as the first of them, a sentence of the same shape as the second may be asserted'. Here we are talking about *the same* shape, i.e. using a universal name-determining functor. Also when we say 'sentence' we are bound to explain what we mean by that word, and this cannot be done otherwise than indicating or describing shapes common to several bodies (heaps of dry ink).[1] Now such words like 'the shape of

---

[1] It will be not without interest to exemplify these in a concrete case, and we shall choose as such a text of N. Goodman and W. V. Quine, from their well-known article *Steps Toward a Constructive Nominalism*,(The Journal of Symbolic Logic 12,1947, 105–122, p.112). There will be a double benefit in it as the authors not only supply a very convenient instance, but also supply it while supporting the opposite theory. Here is the text: ...the characters of our language are not these abstract shapes – which we, as nominalists, cannot countenance – but rather concrete marks or inscriptions. We can, however, apply shape-predicates to such individuals; thus 'Vee x' will mean that the object x is a vee (i.e. a 'v' – shaped inscription), and 'AC x' will mean that x is an accent (i.e. a '''' – shaped inscription), and 'LPar x' will mean that x is a left parenthesis, and 'RPar x' will mean that x is a right parenthesis, and 'Str x' will mean x is a stroke (a '|' shaped inscription), and 'Ep x' will mean that x is an epsilon.

tee' must be semantically meaningful, in order that we might recognize *which* heap of dry ink is a tee. And that means on our assumption that there are semantic meanings corresponding to the functors in the metalanguage. And as metalanguage is a language in which we are talking about bodies (heaps of dry ink), there is absolutely no reason why we should be prevented from using a similarly meaningful language on the object-level, talking about other bodies or any objects at all.

It may be noted that by stating that the only universal meaningful symbols we need are functors i.e. that the only meanings we are bound to admit are the meanings of such functors, we do not reject the existence of other meanings, e.g. of class-names, relation-names, etc. We think that, as we can construct class-names and relation-names, we also have class-concepts and relation-concepts. But those are *constructs* and can be analyzed in terms of meanings of functors.

The second question is, if those unavoidable universal meaningful functors must be *univocal*. The direct insight supplies, we think, a positive answer; but there is also at least one pragmatic argument in favour of it. For, suppose that all symbols would be ambiguous, it is very difficult to see how communication between men would be at all possible – while such communication is a fact. On the other hand, it seems that it is impossible to state correctly a theory asserting that all symbols are ambiguous, without using some symbols univocally. This argument is closely analogous to one which will be formulated below against the similarity theory concerning the PU for real entities; we shall therefore not anticipate it here.

6. Statement of the PU for phenomenal realities

We shall consider now our fourth level, that of phenomenal realities and start with the statement of three theses which we believe evident.

We stated already above that we do classify things and cannot do otherwise. We say now:

(*1*) *Some of our classifications are not quite arbitrary.* This must be qualified in two ways. First, the symbol we attach to such or to such other class of things is, of course, arbitrary; we could e.g. call handkerchiefs 'bottles' and bottles 'handkerchiefs'; but the fact that we make here two classes and ascribe such individual to one of them is not arbitrary.

Second, we may arrange the things in *different* classes. Suppose there are three objects, such that

$$\sim \phi x \cdot \psi x \cdot \chi x$$
$$\phi y \cdot \sim \psi y \cdot \chi y$$
$$\phi z \cdot \psi z \cdot \sim \chi z .$$

We may classify them in three ways: (1) by ϕ : the class will contain y and z but not x as elements; (2) by ψ: it will then contain x, and z; (3) by χ: it will contain x and y. In that way also the classification is arbitrary, namely the choice of the aspect under which we classify them. But given that choice, the operation is – at least sometimes – not arbitrary. Thus, given that we classify our objects, by χ, it is *not* arbitrary that we leave z out. This does not depend on our will.

It may be even thought that *no* classification is quite arbitrary, as we might find in *every* set of objects a reason for conceiving them as one class. Would it be so, our freedom of choice of the way we classify things would be greater than in our hypothesis. But even in that case we could point to sub-sets of the universal class of things, which would be conceived as classes not arbitrarily, but because of something independent from our will.

(2) *Whenever a classification is not quite arbitrary, there is something in the classified things which justifies that classification.* This is not just another formulation of (1) as it asserts that the reason is *in the things* classified. The passage from (1) to (2) has been, as a fact, rejected by those who admit (1) but think, that the non-arbitrary reason for classification may lie elsewhere than in the things. The main representatives of that view are the epistemologic idealists and the Platonists.

According to idealists, the things 'in themselves' do not contain any factor justifying our classifications; whatever justifies it has been brought in by our minds, by the 'transcendental apperception' or by similar, more or less mythical entities. But this is surely not a serious argument against our statement which is about the *phenomenal* world. We are not interested here to know who *made* the bottles, if that was the bottlemaker of the 'transcendental apperception'; the only thing we are interested in is the obvious fact, that, whoever made them, the bottles are such as to supply a foundation for our classifications.

According to Platonists, the justification for our classifications is to be looked for in the idea which is 'beyond' the classified things. To which we say, first, that we do not believe that there is anything as the idea of the bottle, except in a mind; and, second, that even if there were such idea, there would still remain the obvious fact that a classifying scientist does not look for a foundation of his classifications to the idea, but to the things. And, most Platonists seem to admit that the idea is 'participated' in the phenomenal things, which is precisely what we want, because this means that there still is something in the things which justifies our classifications.

(3) Consequently, there are things so connected one with the other that this connection justifies our classifications.

That connection is a *relation*. There *is* such a relation. The PU for the real world is now: what is that relation? [1]

7. The two theories

There are, so it seems, two and *only* two serious theories proposed to answer our problem. We shall call these 'the similarity theory' and 'the identity theory'.

(1) Similarity theory: the link between the classified things consists in their similarity. This must be understood, it seems, as a symmetric and reflexive relation. At the same time the theory denies any identity – total or partial – of the classified things.

(2) Identity theory: the link between the classified things is constituted by the identity of certain aspect or aspects, in other terms of certain properties inherent in all classified objects. That relation of identity must be thought as holding between those aspects (and *not* between the things classified). It is, obviously, a symmetrical, reflexive, and transitive relation.

The partisans of the similarity theory have sometimes been called 'nominalists', while the term of 'Platonism' has been frequently applied to the partisans of the identity theory. Both qualifications seem to be unjustified. For members of the first group do not pretend that universals are 'bare names'; they admit a certain foundation for them; and members of the other are not, by the sole fact of admitting an identity of aspects,

[1] This is, in traditional terms, one aspect of the problem of the foundation of universals. But as we reject universals in the phenomenal world there is for us no such problem here: it arises only on the level of objective meanings.

committed to 'occult and abstract entities'. Let us, therefore, keep to our terms of 'similarity' and 'identity'.

The above theories are the only two which may be considered as serious attempts to answer the question about the nature of the relation linking the classified things. It may be remarked that still another view has been sometimes proposed, namely, a theory which we will term 'bit-theory'. It teaches that the things classified may be conceived as bits (physical parts) of the whole (an individual) composed of all of them; in that case e.g. all bottles would be conceived as one individual and each bottle as a part of it. This doctrine, whatever be its value for other purposes, cannot be recognized as a serious alternative view to the similarity and identity theories. For, suppose the things have to be considered as such wholes; then it is immediately apparent that there is at least one thing *common* to them, namely the being-a-part of that individual – and so the theory is just a special case of the identity theory. Moreover, this is a necessary but not a sufficient condition for the classification of things scattered in space (or time); for, in order to classify them, we must also perceive something in the things themselves which justifies such classification; and that something will be either a similarity or an identity of some properties. Consequently this doctrine is not an alternative theory of universals in the phenomenal world.

8. On properties [1]

It will be noticed that the identity theory makes use of an ontological presupposition which is not necessary for the similarity theory: it assumes namely that there are properties, not only things – while the other theory does not assume it. The partisans of the similarity theory developed recently an ontological doctrine, which explicitly rejects properties; this doctrine may be termed, from its founder, 'Leśniewski's ontology'. It has to be discussed first.

According to Leśniewski, the phenomenal world is composed exclusively of individuals and contains no properties at all. This is to say that the world is completey unstratified, that it contains only one sort of entities, as far as the ontological status is concerned.

A criterion which considerably helps in the formulation and defense of

---

[1] The term 'property' is used here as in contemporary mathematical logic; its Latin equivalent is not 'proprium' but rather 'nota'.

that theory has been supplied by Quine. He states that 'to be is to be the value of a variable.' Goodman and Quine construe then all functors not as variables, but as 'schematic' or 'dummy letters' (somewhat like the so-called 'constants' of the *Principia, 'a'*). Those cannot have values; and, consequently, there *is* nothing in the phenomenal world which would correspond to them as a correlate. Once such functors are bound (as they must be e.g. when defining identity or in mathematics) this procedure cannot be applied; but then Goodman and Quine consider the formula as semantically meaningless, in the way described above (§5) – while no quantified functors and, consequently, no values of variable functors are needed in the metalinguistic rules they use.

This ontology we reject on intuitive [1] grounds. We see the world as stratified, namely, as composed of subjects qualified by properties and, consequently, as such, that, when we state truly e.g. 'ϕa', there is something in the phenomenal world which corresponds not only to 'a', but also to 'ϕ'.

The above view is supported by the following epistemological argument. It has been mentioned above (§3) that every part of the working language may be analyzed into symbols belonging to one of the five primitive syntactical categories, those of individual names, monadic, name-determining functors, existential quantifiers, sentences and of the stroke or amphec. Another important result of the modern mathematical-logical analysis of language is that the category of individual names does not need to be represented by any *constant* name. Those can always be, first, replaced by descriptions; then descriptions are replaced in use by formulas containing *only* variable names, name-determining functors, quantifiers and strokes. But if so, everything which we can say about the phenomenal world can be said by means of functors. We need no individual names at all, except as variables, i.e. as *blanks*; which means, that the meaning of such names is purely operational.

Suppose now that, as Leśniewski's ontology assumes, there is no correlate to those functors in the phenomenal world; then we must say that we do not say *anything* about that world. Because whatever we say, we do so with functors. But we most certainly *do* say something about the phenomenal world. Consequently, the ontology under consideration

---

[1] Intuition is here opposed to discourse, not to abstraction.

must be rejected. The only alternative seems to be an extreme scepticism.

It will be noted that the rejection of that doctrine does *not* commit us to the assumption of any abstract entities in the phenomenal world. We do not posit the extra-mental existence of such entities, and have never been able to discover the slightest trace of them in the world. What the rejection of Leśniewski's ontology entails is the admission that there are two strata in the phenomenal reality: that of subjects (things) and that of properties, both being perfectly individual.[1]

Along with Leśniewski's ontology, we reject Quine's criterion. If the world is stratified and contains at least two sorts of entities with a different ontological status, then the expression 'to be' will have different meanings in its application to the two sorts, to things and to properties. While the criterion stated by Quine is admissible in regard to the former, it is wrong if applied to the latter: for a property, to be is not to be a value of a variable but *to qualify the value of a variable*. Consequently to state that there is something meant by 'ϕ' is to say '$(\exists x) \cdot \phi x$' and not '$(\exists \phi) \cdot \phi x$'. The last formula is misleading, as it seems to attribute to the property the same kind of existence which is attributed to the values of x. Once we write '$(\exists \phi) \cdot \phi x$' we turn the property into a thing.

We meet here a curious problem which will recur again later. One would think, perhaps, that we may use a different kind of quantifier for functors, thus evading the difficulty. But this does not seem to be the case. It looks as if we were concerned here with something which simply cannot be stated in other terms than '$(\exists x) \cdot \phi x$'. This is, by the way, not a unique case in logic. The late Reichenbach tried to symbolize the relation between ϕ and x when ϕx; that there is such a relation is obvious. But when he symbolized it by what he called a 'logical constant' and wrote '$\alpha[\phi x]$' it appeared immediately that he has again a relation between α and ϕx, which he cannot symbolize. The situation seems to be similar here.

9. *The similarity theory rejected*

This theory is the only acceptable one for a partisan of Leśniewski's

---

[1] The following suggestion has been made to the author: These strata must be more than predicable accidents; they therefore imply an ontological distinction between substance and predicamental accidents.

ontology, and it would be also the most convenient for *any* individualist. Unfortunately, it meets with such serious difficulties that is must be discarded. The main difficulties of that doctrine are the the following.

(1) It renders every explicit statement on classified things cumbrous and complicated. Wherever the partisan of the identity theory can take e.g.

$$(9.1) \quad (\exists\, x, y) \cdot \phi x \cdot \phi y \cdot x \neq y$$

for an adequate statement of a fact, the follower of the similarity theory is bound to consider it as an elliptical formula, an abbreviation of something like the following (meaning of the functors as in (§2):

$$(9.2) \quad (\exists\, f, g, x, y) \cdot f\,Hg \cdot f\,Px \cdot g\,Py \cdot x \neq y$$

which is (contrary to 9.1) a metalogical and cumbrous formula. In case where there would be three classified objects, he would even be bound to write something like:

$$(9.3) \quad (\exists\, f, g, h, x, y, z) \cdot f\,Hg \cdot g\,Hh \cdot h\,Hx \cdot f\,Px \cdot g\,Py \cdot h\,Pz \cdot x \neq y \cdot y \neq z \cdot$$
$$\cdot z \neq x$$

whereas the partisan of the identity theory could be content with

$$(9.4) \quad (\exists\, x, y, z) \cdot \phi x \cdot \phi y \cdot \phi z \cdot x \neq y \cdot y \cdot \neq z \cdot z \neq x$$

This is, admittedly, not a decisive argument, but still an argument.

(2) The similarity theory cannot be stated otherwise than in terms of the identity theory. Even in (9.2) there are two '*P*', in (9.3) there are three '*H*', three '*P*', and three '$\neq$'; what those functors mean is something common to several distinct individuals – for e.g. if $f\,Hg$, then f belongs to the domain of H, and so does g because of '$g\,Hf$' etc. Formulae like (9.3) may be again explained in terms of the similarity theory but at each step the language of the identity theory must be used and, as we have to stop somewhere, the latter will be always presupposed, if we wish to explain what we mean by the similarity theory.

(3) The classification based on similarity presupposes identity; thus the similarity theory presupposes the identity theory. As a matter of fact, not *any* sort of similarity is sufficient for a given classification. Would it be so, then, as there is a certain similarity between every object and every other object, there would be only one possible way of classification, while there are, manifestly, many such ways and some of them are, as we have seen above (§6) based on something in the classified objects. That something must be, obviously a similarity in a certain *respect*. We may classify

132

things by colour or by shape, or by weight and so on; but there must always be something, some respect, *by which* we classify. Now that respect is obviously *common* to the classified things. E.g., if we classify things by colour, it may be that they are only similar in that respect; but they still must be, both of them, *coloured*. In other terms, there must be an identity of a certain property: and that is what the identity theory asserts.

10. The identity theory

We are thus committed to the identity theory. This, however, meets with a difficulty known already in antiquity [1] and recently restated by Leśniewski. It may be stated in the following way:

Suppose our (9.1) is true, i.e. that there are two things x and y such that they are non-identical and yet have an identical property ϕ. As they are not identical there is (by definition of identity) at least one property, say ψ, such that $\psi x \cdot \sim \psi y$. We have, consequently, $\phi x \cdot \psi x$ but $\phi y \cdot \sim \psi y$. Consider now ϕ in x; it is in x together with ψ; let us call 'ϑ' the property of being-in-x-together-with-ψ; this second-level property ϑ will belong to ϕ in x, but will, obviously, not belong to ϕ in y; thus there will be at least one (second-level) property which belongs to ϕ in x and does not belong to ϕ in y; and this entails, by the definition of identity, that the two cases of ϕ are not identical. But it has been supposed that they are identical.

It must be confessed that the partisan of a theory which admits universals in things would not be embarrassed by this argument; he would simply state, that he considers both ϕ's as being identical, and, consequently, whatever is the property of ϑ in the first instance – ϑ included – is also a property of ϕ in the second instance, those being *the same* property. And he would legitimately ask for a formalization of the argument. But such formalization either presupposes what he denies, or is invalid (the reason of the invalidity being that it is not possible to state a correct definition

---

[1] Cf. Sextus Empiricus, *Hyp. Pyrr.* B 227.

[2] The following complementary consideration has been suggested: The same argument could be used by anyone who denies subsistent universals but admits a foundation for universals in things. He likewise considers both ϕ's to be identical not in their individuated subjects, but in the consideration of his mind as abstracted from individuating matter. Again a formalized refutation would be impossible. (There is, of course, no possibility of *reductio ad absurdum,* because the possibility of such an argument presupposes an absurdity in the first place. The only absurdity that could arise would be traceable to a misunderstanding of *abstrahentium non est mendacium.*)

of 'ϑ' without admitting something rejected by the adversary). This is one instance of the failure of the *reductio ad absurdum* in the domain of the PU². But for an individualist the argument has some interest. He namely admits, that the two instances of ϕ are still distinct. Everything which is a property of one object is *its* property and is in no way the property of the other. Thus the argument is relevant to him.

It forces him namely to state that by 'identity' as applied to properties he does *not* mean the same sort of identity which is applied to individuals. If we symbolize the former by '$\underset{s}{=}$',

(10.1) $\phi \underset{s}{=} \psi \cdot \equiv \cdot (\vartheta) \cdot \vartheta(\phi) \equiv \vartheta(\psi)$

does *not* hold: not *every* second-level property of the 'common' property in one of its instances is its property in another instance. That this is so, should be intuitively evident: if things are, say scarlet, and thus have the scarletness in common, it does not follow that every *shade* of scarlet in one instance is also the shade of scarlet in the second instance. The identity ascribed to properties by the theory is a *partial* identity.

If we try, however, to formulate more precisely what we mean by 'partial' we meet considerable difficulties. As first approach the following formula would appear as convenient:

(10.2) $\phi \underset{s}{=} \psi \cdot \equiv : (\vartheta) : \vartheta \, \varepsilon \, \kappa \cdot \supset \cdot \vartheta(\phi) \equiv \vartheta(\psi)$.

But this would not do for two reasons. First, 'κ' must be defined: and there seems to be no means of defining it, except in terms of formulas, in which symbols like '$\phi x \cdot \phi y$' would recur; second, there seems to be no way to define 'κ' extensively. And in this paper we are not interested in intensional definitions.

There remains however another possibility. Contrary to the situation concerning the subjects, there are *two* extensional definitions of identity for properties; the first is analogous to that of subjects, it is our (10.1); the second is:

(10.3) $\phi \underset{s}{=} \psi \cdot \equiv \cdot (x) \cdot \phi x \equiv \psi x$.

This definition does not give rise immediately to the difficulties stated above. But we do not know, if (10.3) does not entail, in the frame of a normal 'working' logic, (9.1). Would this be the case, the contradiction would still be present. This problem will have to be solved before it can be said that (10.3) represents any contribution to the statement of our problem.

11. On S-identity

The main result of the above discussion is, that we are bound to admit, from the point of view of individualism, two different kinds of identity. The first kind, defined in (10.1), may be termed 'N-identity'; the second, of which (10.2) and (10.3) are attempts of a definition, we shall call S-identity. It seems to us that N-identity is a relation proper to things, while S-identity is something which belongs to properties. We meet here, consequently, another aspect of that fundamental distinction of two ontological levels, the level of things and the level of properties. As it is meaningless to ascribe to properties that sort of existence, which belongs to things, so, it seems, it is hopeless to try to explain in terms of N-identity, proper to subjects, the S-identity of properties.

The failure to understand this lies, we believe, at the bottom both of extreme realism and nominalism. From our point of view, those two doctrines do not offer a wrong *solution* of the PU: they simply do not *state* it at all. For *the PU is,* to an individualist, first of all, *the problem how to explain identity.*[1] It is preposterous to him, to try to replace it by N-identity i.e. to assert the existence of universals in the world; but it is equally preposterous to deny the existence of specific identity. The problem is correctly stated only, when the identity is admitted.

Once this is done, however, not one problem, but rather a class of different problems rises. What are the syntactical properties of specific identity? Can it be reduced to other concepts and how? How do universal meanings arise, given that the starting point is just specific identity and nothing else? What is the status of properties of properties, of classes of classes, etc.?

In the present state of logic and semantics, we are prepared to study at least some of those problems – the first has been, we think, even solved by the *Principia,* and we believe that the second should be answered by the negative. But for other problems, the tools are still lacking. Thus, in order to deal with the triadic relation between realities, meanings and linguistic symbols, we would need a semantics of a different kind than the current one, which knows only of a dyadic semantic relation, between linguistic symbols and realities. If such semantics would be built up, perhaps the problem of classes etc. could be dealt with in a more convenient

---

[1] By which is not meant that this is the *only* problem of universals.

way than by the Quine-Goodman method. And, finally, the mathematical-logical study of other aspects of the PU would probably require far more powerful logical and semantical instruments than those we possess now. To mention just one aspect, we do not have any conveniently developed theory of polyadic relations in logic.[1]

---

[1] It is not implied that there is no correct solution of the fundamental aspects of the PU: on the contrary, the author thinks that such solution has been found many centuries ago. But we still lack tools for a mathematical-logical elaboration of that solution similar to that offered a few years ago by the author for the problem of analogy.